# MINIA1 RAILWAYS
## OF GREAT BRITAIN & IRELAND

FIRST EDITION

Peter Bryant & Dave Holroyde

**PLATFORM 5**

Published by Platform 5 Publishing Ltd.,
3 Wyvern House, Sark Road, Sheffield S2 4HG, England.

Printed in England by Berforts Information Press, Eynsham, Oxford.

ISBN 978 1 902336 93 0

2

# CONTENTS

**Front Cover Photograph:** The Ravenglass and Eskdale Railway celebrated its 50th anniversary at the beginning of May 2011. Here 10 "Northern Rock" is seen at the head of one of the anniversary weekend specials. **Dane Murdoch**

**Left:** The oldest locomotive on the Ravenglass & Eskdale Railway is 3 "River Irt" built by Arthur Heywood. It is seen here between duties at Ravenglass on 8 November 2008. **Simon Metcalf**

**Back Cover Photograph:** Two of the best-known miniature railways are the Romney, Hythe & Dymchurch in Kent and the Ravenglass & Eskdale in Cumbria. In 2011, RHDR 1 "Green Goddess" visited the RER and is seen here at Irton Road, double-heading a service with RER resident 9 "River Mite" on 2 May 2011. **Dane Murdoch**

# INTRODUCTION

The miniature railway now occupies an important role in the overall scene for the railway enthusiast, with many superb and high quality layouts all over the United Kingdom to delight the discerning enthusiast and members of the general public. Indeed, miniature railways are now more popular than ever before.

For the purposes of this book we have defined miniature railways as including all gauges from 21 inch gauge down to 7¼ inch gauge. Of course, many railways operate on gauges smaller than 7¼ inch gauge, but these are often portable in nature (rolling stock particularly, if not the track!) and are therefore not included within the scope of this book. Where smaller or multi-gauge track is present at locations covered by the book, details of these gauges are provided under the specific railway entry.

We have endeavoured to include details of all commercial miniature railways open to the public during 2012 and also club tracks which open to the public at least once every week in the summer season. For most locations we have included a detailed listing of the locomotive fleet, but please be aware that most locos operating on club tracks are kept at the homes of club members, so not all the locos listed will be seen on a visit. Additionally, some clubs have asked that the locos operating there are not listed and some clubs have asked not to be included in the book at all.

Of course, all miniature railways are narrow gauge railways but the converse is not necessarily true. Many of the miniature railways in this book have locomotives (and sometimes rolling stock) which are models of real or imaginary prototypes of standard or larger gauge types. Even so, some of the lines are genuinely 'minimum gauge railways', doing jobs of work in their own right, without direct inspiration from larger ancestors.

The book is updated to information received by May 2012.

# ACKNOWLEDGEMENTS

We would like to thank all of the miniature railway operators who have contributed information for this book. We have taken every step we can to ensure accuracy of the information, but we would welcome any notifications of corrections or updates to this book; please send any comments or amendments to us care of the publisher's address on the title page or by email to updates@platform5.com

**Peter Bryant & Dave Holroyde. May 2012.**

# LAYOUT OF INFORMATION

The Information presented in this book has been divided into 12 geographical areas. Within those areas each location is listed in alphabetical order, with a brief description of the operation and a selection of contact details and technical information.

Locomotives are listed in the following order:

Steam
Steam Outline (S/O - having the appearance of being steam powered but actually diesel/battery/petrol)
Diesel/Battery/Petrol

Within these categories locos are listed on a chronological basis, oldest to newest. Those without known build dates are listed at the end of the category and locomotives under construction are marked U/C.

# ADDRESSES

These are in all cases the addresses of the railways concerned, rather than being postal addresses of the railways' operators.

# TELEPHONE NUMBERS

Where given, these are generally numbers of the location concerned. In a small number of cases the railway operators have permitted us to publish their home or mobile phone numbers. Home numbers are marked (Evenings). Please do not abuse this courtesy by calling at irregular hours.

# OPERATORS

Wherever known these are the individuals or companies responsible for running trains, not necessarily the land or rolling stock owners, or in the case of companies, the company owners.

# WEBSITES

During the lifetime of this book we expect a good number of additional railways will gain websites, and some of the existing sites will change their URL addresses. We recommend http://www.miniaturerailwayworld.co.uk as a good starting point for miniature railway subjects.

# LINE LENGTHS

These are approximate, to the nearest 50 yards. The layout of many lines are quite similar, falling into one of the following four categories

More extensive layouts are described as Complex.

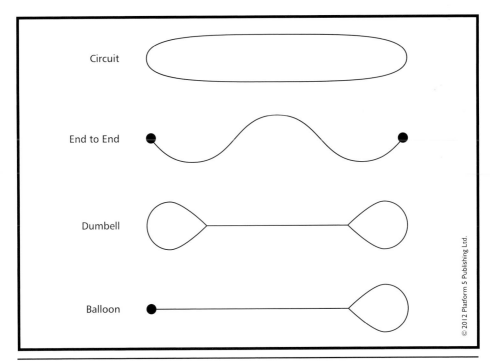

Circuit

End to End

Dumbell

Balloon

© 2012 Platform 5 Publishing Ltd.

# FIRST OPENED

These are the years of the first miniature railway presence on site, not necessarily of the same gauge or necessarily implying continuous service since.

# LOCOMOTIVE NUMBERS AND NAMES

These are shown as carried on the locomotives concerned; where a number is shown in parentheses or a name in quotation marks, the number or name is not actually carried on the locomotive but it is the number or name by which the locomotive is commonly known.

# TYPE

The Whyte notation of wheel arrangement has been used for virtually all steam locomotives and for non-steam locomotives with driving wheels connected by coupling rods. The number of leading wheels is given, followed by the number of driving wheels and then the trailing wheels.

Suffixes are used to denote tank locomotives as follows:

| | |
|---|---|
| T: | Side Tank |
| PT: | Pannier Tank |
| ST: | Saddle Tank |
| WT: | Well Tank |
| VBT: | Vertical Boiler with Tank |
| +T: | Tank Locomotive with Tender |

For example, 2-4-0ST would be a saddle tank locomotive with 2 leading wheels, 4 driving wheels and no trailing wheels.

For locomotives where driving wheels are connected by means other than coupling rods, w is used to indicate powered axles. For example, 4-4w means two four wheeled bogies, with the rear bogie powered on all four wheels. The following abbreviations are used to denote the power source of such locomotives:

| | |
|---|---|
| BE: | Battery Electric Locomotive |
| BER: | Battery Electric Railcar |
| DE: | Diesel Locomotive with Electric Transmission |
| DER: | Diesel Electric Railcar |
| DH: | Diesel Locomotive with Hydraulic Transmission |
| DHR: | Diesel Hydraulic Railcar |
| DM: | Diesel Locomotive with Mechanical Transmission |
| GM: | Gas Locomotive with Mechanical Transmission |
| GH: | Gas Locomotive with Hydraulic Transmission |
| PE: | Petrol Locomotive with Electric Transmission |
| PH: | Petrol Locomotive with Hydraulic Transmission |
| PM: | Petrol Locomotive with Mechanical Transmission |
| PMR: | Petrol Mechanical Railcar |
| RE: | Electric with Power from Third Rail |
| TG: | Steam Tank Locomotive with Geared transmission |
| WER: | Electric with Power from Overhead Wire |

Steam Outline locomotives are denoted by S/O.

# BUILDER

Some Company names have been abbreviated e.g Severn Lamb Ltd to just Severn Lamb. In some cases trading names have been used for individuals or partnerships.

# OPENING HOURS

It would be impossible for us to include detailed opening hours of each location, which would be lengthy and subject to change. Some lines operate all year round, particularly those which are near to major centres of population rather than in seaside areas or amusement parks. Some railways only open weather permitting. In virtually all cases fine Sundays during the summer school holidays are the best times to find miniature railways busy. If at all in doubt, telephone or visit the railway's website before travelling to visit a specific railway.

# PHOTOGRAPHY AND OTHER MATTERS

Miniature railways offer much for the avid photographer; trains are frequent and there is much variety between the different locations. Always start your visit by riding round on the train. It's the best way to see all the locations on offer, and to give something to the humble operator. Always gain permission before crossing fences or entering the shed area. If the other locomotives are locked up don't expect a guided tour in mid afternoon; first thing or last thing are generally the best times.

Many operators of railways in this book are enthusiasts themselves to some extent, but the view from the footplate can be surprisingly different to that of the visitor. If you travel 150 miles on a wet Tuesday in June to find the railway deserted, or the steam engine broken, don't blame us, we're just the authors. If on the other hand you have an enjoyable time, then mention this book and say we sent you!

# A BRIEF HISTORICAL SURVEY

Man has made models since time immemorial, to show what a finished object would look like, or for the challenge and subsequent satisfaction of its completion. Then along came Sir Arthur Percival Heywood, who took this to a new level, believing that a 15 inch gauge locomotive could perform a useful job of work. He built a spectacular railway up the hill behind his house and his book "Minimum Gauge Railways" led to the construction of the railway at Eaton Hall in Cheshire in 1896. Although his ideas never really caught on in his lifetime, he is revered as the founder of small railways designed in their own right, rather than as models.

It was in the USA where miniature railways really took off, when the Cagney Brothers first exploited the idea of small railways for pleasure. Some of their train sets made it over here and inspired W J Bassett-Lowke and Henry Greenly to design and build miniature railways. Bassett-Lowke was the businessman who saw the potential and Greenly the brilliant designer, whose legacy can still be seen at locations in this book. Bassett-Lowke built their 15 inch gauge Little Giant in 1905 and were soon supplying complete locos, castings and drawings in 7¼ inch, 9½ inch and 15 inch gauges.

In 1915 they took over an abandoned 3 foot gauge, 7 mile long mineral line at Ravenglass in Cumberland and re-gauged it to 15 inch. Since then the Ravenglass and Eskdale Railway has gone from strength to strength, especially since being taken over by the preservation society in 1960. Greenly's ultimate achievement came in 1927 with the world famous Romney, Hythe and Dymchurch Railway. This 14 mile long line from Hythe to Dymchurch was conceived as a main line in miniature by Captain Howey and designed by Greenly. Its 1/3 scale locos, mainly LNER pacifics and 4-8-2s are still in use today, over 80 years later.

The 9½ inch gauge wasn't as popular and was replaced after 1910 by the well proven 10¼ inch gauge. This gauge reached its zenith with the Surrey Border and Camberley Railway, the most ambitious 10¼ inch gauge line in the world, which unfortunately had to close at the start of the Second World War.

At the end of the war, as things began to return to normal, leisure attractions regained their popularity. Mothballed lines re-opened and a large number of new lines were built. New builders and designers, such as David Curwen and Carland Engineering built new locomotives and coaching stock for this new generation of lines. Curwen's legacy can be seen in the locos he built for the Audley End Railway in Essex.

Severn Lamb entered the market in 1967, initially with their Curwen designed "Western" and "Rio Grande" petrol locos, followed by steam locos in gauges from 7¼ inch to 15 inch. They later moved into the 2 foot and 3 foot gauges, mainly for export, but their miniature locos are all still in regular use at lines throughout the UK. Other new builders have included Cromar White Railways, Mardyke Miniature Railways, Roanoke and Knightley Light Railways.

The 7¼ inch gauge has been with us since 1909, but really took off post war with the superb lines at the Great Cockcrow and the greatly missed Hilton Valley railways. Later lines such as the Dobwalls Railroad and Jim Haylock's masterpiece, the Moors Valley Railway followed. Locos in this gauge have moved on from the initial 1/8 scale main line prototypes, to the large narrow gauge prototypes we see today. Little did Roger Marsh realise what he was unleashing when he first designed his sit-in Tinkerbell 0-4-2T in 1968! Many model engineering clubs have built ground level tracks to cater for their members building larger locos. There are several large tracks, such as those at Echills Wood and Coate, near Swindon.

Post war, new railways have also been built in 12¼ inch gauge, of which the best known are Fairbourne Steam Railway, re-gauged from 15 inch by John Ellerton in the 1980s, the currently closed Exmoor Steam Railway and the late lamented line at Ashorne Hall. The Exmoor Steam Railway has built a number of steam locos in this gauge, as well as in 7¼ inch, 10¼ inch and 15 inch gauge.

When you visit UK miniature lines, you will find a range of lines from over 100 years old to the present day, of scale main line to huge narrow gauge outlines, from short circuits to large complex layouts. It's a fascinating world out there, so go out and explore it and tell the operators we sent you!

# AREA 1: SOUTH WEST

Cornwall, Devon, Dorset, Somerset, Wiltshire.

## BEER HEIGHTS LIGHT RAILWAY

This line is built high on a hill with deep cuttings, high embankments, and a long tunnel under the car park. Immaculately maintained with full signalling and realistic lineside buildings, the railway is one of the finest in the country. Usually operates weekdays from April to October, plus Saturdays and Sundays in the main summer season.

**Address:** Pecorama Pleasure Gardens and Exhibition, Underleys, Beer, Near Seaton, Devon, EX12 3NA.
**Telephone:** 01297 21542.
**OS Grid Ref:** SY 224893.
**Operator:** Howe & Davis Ltd.
**Website:** www.pecorama.info
**Gauge:** 7¼ inch.
**Line Length:** 1800 yards, complex.
**First Opened:** 1975.

Site entry fee.

| No | Name | Type | Builder | Built |
|----|------|------|---------|-------|
| 5 | Linda | 2-4-0ST+T | J Clarke/TMA Engineering | 1971 |
| 3 | Dickie | 0-4-2 | D Curwen | 1976 |
| 4 | Thomas II | 0-4-2 | R Marsh | 1979 |
| | Yeo | 2-6-2T | Milner Engineering | 1979 |
| 7 | Mr P | 2-4-2 | BHLR/Western NG | 1997 |
| 8 | Gem | 0-6-0T+T | Demslow/BHLR | 1998 |
| | Samastipur | 0-4-2T | Exmoor Steam Railway | 1999 |
| 1 | Otter | 2-4-2 | Western Narrow Gauge | 2004 |
| 9 | Claudine | 2-4-4T | BHLR/Western NG | 2005 |
| 6 | Jimmy | 4-4wDH | Severn Lamb | 1986 |
| 10 | Alfred | 4w-4wBER | BHLR | 2003 |
| | | 4w-4wGM | BHLR | U/C |

## BICKINGTON STEAM RAILWAY

This line has an imposing main station at Trago Central, from where trains descend over a 23 pier viaduct, before looping round across themselves several times and then climbing back again. At one point there are six parallel tracks all on different levels. "E. R. Calthrop" is a model of a 2 foot 6inch gauge locomotive which once ran on the Leek & Manifold Railway in Derbyshire. "Blanche of Lancaster" once achieved fame by appearing on TV in an episode of "The Avengers", filmed at the Stapleford Miniature Railway.

**Address:** Trago Mills Shopping & Leisure Centre, Stover, Near Newton Abbot, Devon, TQ12 6JB.
**Telephone:** 01626 821 111.
**OS Grid Ref:** SX 821742.
**Operator:** Trago Mills.
**Website:** www.trago.co.uk
**Gauge:** 10¼ inch.
**Line Length:** 1¾ mile, return trip; 2¼ miles, balloon loop.
**First Opened:** 1988.

| No | Name | Type | Builder | Built |
|----|------|------|---------|-------|
| 750 | Blanche of Lancaster | 4-4-2 | D Curwen | 1948 |
| 1 | E.R. Calthrop | 2-6-4T | Coleby Simkins | 1974 |
| | Alice | 2-6-0 | Simkins & Vere | 1984 |
| 24 | (Sandy River) | 2-6-2 | Coleby Simkins/Alcock/Vere | 1991 |
| D5910 | | 4w-4wDH | D Nicholson | 1987 |

# BOURNEMOUTH & DISTRICT SOME

The club moved here from their former site at Kings Park. The track is mainly amongst trees and is a "dog bone" shape with two parallel tracks in the centre.

**Address:** Littledown Centre, Chaseside, Castle Lane East, Bournemouth, Dorset, BH7 7DX.
**OS Grid Ref:** SZ 122937
**Operator:** Bournemouth & District Society of Model Engineers.
**Website:** www.littledownrailway.co.uk
**Gauge:** 3½ inch/5 inch/7¼ inch.
**Line Length:** 600 yards, elevated circuit.

# CLEVEDON MINIATURE RAILWAY

The locomotive here is the smallest gauge of Severn Lamb "Rio Grande" yet built. 595 was its owner's number before his retirement from the police service. The circuit runs around an open field; steam once operated here many years ago. The line operates all year round subject to weather conditions.

**Address:** Salthouse Fields, Clevedon, Somerset, BS21 7XP.
**Telephone:** 01275 872670 (Evenings).
**OS Grid Ref:** ST 398710.
**Operator:** Messrs A & R Giles.
**Gauge:** 9½ inch.
**Line Length:** 900 yards, circular.
**First Opened:** 1952.

| No | Name | Type | Builder | Built |
|---|---|---|---|---|
| 595 | Charles Henry | S/O 2-8-0PH | Severn Lamb | 1976 |

# COATE WATER MINIATURE RAILWAY (NORTH WILTS MES)

A long ground level track in a country park, comprising a main circuit and two loops.

**Address:** Coate Water Country Park, Swindon, Wiltshire, SN3 6AA.
**OS Grid Ref:** SU 179827.
**Operator:** North Wilts Model Engineering Society.
**Website:** www.nwmes.info
**Gauge:** 5 inch/7¼ inch.
**Line Length:** 880 yards, complex.
**First Opened:** 1965.

| No | Name | Type | Builder | Built |
|---|---|---|---|---|
| | Perculator | 0-4-0ST | R Barratt | 1978 |
| 9900 | William J Clarke | 4-6-0 | W Clarke | 1992 |
| | Rak-Rat | 0-4-0T | R Thompson | 1992 |
| 61789 | Loch Laidon | 2-6-0 | J Drury | 1996 |
| 587 | | 2-6-0 | A Church | 1998 |
| | Eva | 0-6-0WT | J Middleton | 2000 |
| 6868 | Penrhos Grange | 4-6-0 | A Newbery | 2005 |
| 92203 | | 2-10-0 | R Statton | 2008 |
| 92204 | | 2-10-0 | R Statton | 2008 |
| 70052 | Firth of Tay | 4-6-2 | M Foley | 2008 |
| 60080 | Dick Turpin | 4-6-2 | Modelworks/Dixon | 2009 |
| 70054 | Dornoch Firth | 4-6-2 | Winson/Hand | 2010 |
| 1366 | | 0-6-0PT | R Barratt | 2011 |
| 2397 | | 2-8-2 | R Martin | 2011 |
| 4470 | Great Northern | 4-6-2 | | |
| | Sam | 4wBE | J Bond | 1990 |
| 86262 | | 4w-4BE | R Statton | 2002 |
| | Fred | 4wPH | Roanoke | 2004 |
| 66625 | | 6w-6wBE | Abbots ME | 2009 |
| D5094 | | 4w-4wBE | | |

▲ 9 "Claudine" stands alongside 7 "Mr P" and visiting locomotive "Finn Macool", all three locomotives in steam at the Beer Heights Light Railway on 9 October 2010. **Dave Holroyde**

▼ 24, the impressive "Sandy River" 2-6-2, is seen at the main station of the Bickington Steam Railway on 10 October 2010. **Dave Holroyde**

# CRICKET ST THOMAS RAILWAY

This line runs around part of Cricket St Thomas Lakes & Gardens, from Woodland Walk Station along the side of a valley, before swinging round over a substantial viaduct known as the "Chinese Bridge" to terminate at Fennochi's Junction. The train, which consists of an Alan Keef steam outline locomotive and 4 articulated carriages, was refurbished in 2009 by Hunslet Engine Company and is now leased to the park.

**Address:** Cricket St Thomas Lakes & Gardens, Near Chard, Somerset, TA20 4DD.
**Telephone:** 01460 30111.
**OS Grid Ref:** ST 374086.
**Operator:** Warner Leisure Hotels.
**Website:** www.warnerleisurehotels.co.uk
**Gauge:** 15 inch.
**Line Length:** 800 yards, end to end.
**First Opened:** 1975.

Park entry fee.

| No | Name | Type | Builder | Built |
|----|------|------|---------|-------|
| | | S/O 0-6-2DH | Alan Keef | 1995 |

# DEVON RAILWAY CENTRE MINIATURE RAILWAY

This line winds its way around part of this railway centre in Devon. Also on site is a 2 foot gauge railway.

**Address:** Devon Railway Centre, The Station, Bickleigh, Devon, EX16 8RG.
**Telephone:** 01884 855 671.
**OS Grid Ref:** SS 938076.
**Operator:** Devon Railway Centre.
**Website:** www.devonrailwaycentre.co.uk
**Gauge:** 7¼ inch.
**Line Length:** 450 yards, balloon loop.
**First Opened:** 2001.

Site Entry Fee.

| No | Name | Type | Builder | Built |
|----|------|------|---------|-------|
| 7 | | S/O 4wBER | Parkside | 2002 |
| (D7011) | | 4w-4BE | Cromar White | 1969 |
| | Alfie | 0-4-0PM | C R Chandler | c1978 |
| 109 | | 4w-4PH | A Bimpson | 1982 |
| | | 4wPH | Pfeifferbahn | 1993 |
| | | 4w-4BER | Stoford MLS | c1995 |

# EARTHQUAKE CANYON RAILWAY

An end to end line with a station, tunnel, and bridge over a stream.

**Address:** The Wildlife & Dinosaur Adventure Park, Higher Leigh, Combe Martin, Devon, EX34 0NG.
**Telephone:** 01271 882 486.
**OS Grid Ref:** SS 600452.
**Operator:** Mr Butcher.
**Website:** www.devonthemepark.co.uk
**Gauge:** 15 inch
**Line Length:** 500 yards, end to end.
**First Opened:** 1989.

Park entry fee.

| No | Name | Type | Builder | Built |
|----|------|------|---------|-------|
| | | S/O 2-8-0PH | Severn Lamb | 1987 |

# EAST SOMERSET MINIATURE RAILWAY

A short end to end line at the East Somerset Railway's main station at Cranmore. The line is currently being extended to a length of 400 yards.

**Address:** East Somerset Railway, Cranmore, Somerset, BA4 4QP.
**Telephone:** 01963 350 002 (Evenings).
**OS Grid Ref:** ST 667430.
**Operator:** East Somerset Miniature Railway Group.
**Website:** www.eastsomersetrailway.com
**Gauge:** 7¼ inch.
**Line Length:** 200 yards, end to end.
**First Opened:** 2009.

| No | Name | Type | Builder | Built |
|----|------|------|---------|-------|
| | Shirley | 0-4-0ST | J Knight | 1990 |
| 1104 | | 0-4-0T | Caldwell | |
| | Elidir | 0-4-0ST | | |
| | The Jacobite | 4wPH | J Williams | c2010 |
| | Alfred | 0-6-0PH | | |

# EXMOUTH EXPRESS

A short circuit forming part of the sea front amusements; the line passes through the stock shed en route. Steam engines operated here in the 1940s and 1950s, including a Curwen Atlantic.

**Address:** Exmouth Fun Park, Queens Drive, Exmouth, Devon, EX8 2AY.
**Telephone:** 01395 222 545.
**OS Grid Ref:** SY 004802.
**Operator:** Exmouth Fun Park.
**Website:** www.exmouthfunpark.co.uk
**Gauge:** 10¼ inch.
**Line Length:** 150 yards, circular.
**First Opened:** 1949.

Park Entry Fee.

| No | Name | Type | Builder | Built |
|----|------|------|---------|-------|
| | | 4wDM | G M Kichenside | 1978 |

# JUNGLE EXPRESS

Situated adjoining the well known stately home of Lord Bath, the line runs from Longleat Central station through parkland and alongside a lake for half a mile, where sea lions and monkeys can be seen on an island. Hippos sometimes surface. A busy, well established line.

**Address:** Longleat House, Warminster, Wiltshire, BA12 7NW.
**Telephone:** 01985 845 408.
**OS Grid Ref:** ST 808432.
**Operator:** Longleat.
**Website:** www.longleat.co.uk
**Gauge:** 15 inch.
**Line Length:** 1 mile, balloon loop.
**First Opened:** 1965.

Park entry fee.

| No | Name | Type | Builder | Built |
|----|------|------|---------|-------|
| 6 | Rudolph | 0-6-2T | Exmoor Steam Railway | 2004 |
| 5 | Ceawlin | S/O 2-8-2DH | Severn Lamb | 1975 |
| 4 | Lenka | 4-4wDHR | J Hayton | 1984 |
| 7 | Flynn | 0-6-0DH | Alan Keef | 2007 |

▲ Alan Keef built 7 "Flynn" enters Longleat Central on the Jungle Express in July 2010. **Peter Bryant**

▼ 1 "Zebedee" enters the East Wheal Rose loop from the woodland at the Lappa Valley Steam Railway in August 2009. **Peter Bryant**

# JUNGLE EXPRESS

This long established line has its station at the side of the main pathway through the zoo. It runs around the adjacent lake and over two bridges, with views of some of the animals at the zoo whilst en route.

**Address:** Paignton Zoo Environmental Park, Totnes Road, Paignton, Devon, TQ4 7EU.
**Telephone:** 0844 474 2222.
**OS Grid Ref:** SX 878597.
**Operator:** Paignton Zoo Environmental Park.
**Website:** www.paigntonzoo.org.uk
**Gauge:** 10¼ inch.
**Line Length:** 500 yards, circular.
**First Opened:** 1937.

Zoo entry fee.

| No | Name | Type | Builder | Built |
|----|------|------|---------|-------|
| | | 4-4wPM | G&SLE | 1939 |
| 4808 | Peter | 4-4wDM | Nicholson/Wedgewood | 1995 |

# LAPPA VALLEY STEAM RAILWAY

This is the only railway in this book where you can ride upon three different gauges of miniature railway at one location. The 15 inch gauge takes you from the car park at Benny Halt to East Wheal Rose, where there is an historic mine engine house along with a boating lake and other attractions. From there, included in the one charge, you can travel further along the standard gauge trackbed using the 10¼ inch gauge line, or whizz round in circles in a sit-in "APT" set on the 7¼ inch gauge. Founded by Eric Booth, this popular attraction is now owned and operated by his family. Watch out for some interesting technical features, like the cross between a turntable and a sector plate at Benny Halt.

**Address:** St. Newlyn East, Newquay, Cornwall, TR8 5HZ.
**Telephone:** 01872 510 317.
**OS Grid Ref:** SW 839573.
**Operator:** Lappa Valley Railway Company Ltd.
**Website:** www.lappavalley.co.uk
**Gauge:** 15 inch/10¼ inch/7¼ inch.
**Line Length:** 15 inch gauge: 1¼ miles, balloon loop; Newlyn branch line 10¼ inch gauge: 700 yards, end to end; Woodland Railway 7¼ inch gauge: 350 yards, circular.
**First Opened:** 15 inch gauge: 1974; Newlyn branch line: 1995; Woodland Railway: 1978.

### 15 inch gauge:

| No | Name | Type | Builder | Built |
|----|------|------|---------|-------|
| 2 | Muffin | 0-6-0 | Berwyn Engineering | 1967 |
| 1 | Zebedee | 0-6-4T | Severn Lamb | 1974 |
| | Arthur | 4wDM | Lister | 1942 |
| | Gladiator | 4-4wDH | Minirail | 1960 |

### 10¼ inch gauge:

| No | Name | Type | Builder | Built |
|----|------|------|---------|-------|
| | Duke of Cornwall | 4w-4PH | Severn Lamb | 1981 |
| | Eric | 0-6-0DH | Alan Keef | 2008 |

### 7¼ inch gauge:

| No | Name | Type | Builder | Built |
|----|------|------|---------|-------|
| | | 4w-4wPH | Mardyke | c1982 |
| (1005) | | 4-4wPH | Mardyke | 1983 |

# LITTLE WESTERN RAILWAY

This attractive little line is normally operated by a Mardyke "HST" set. "Royal Scot" has recently been cosmetically restored by engineers at the sister Lappa Valley Steam Railway and is here on static display. It was the main motive power along with a Cromar White "Hymek" when the line first opened.

**Address:** Trenance Leisure Park, Newquay, Cornwall, TR7 2HL.
**Telephone:** 01872 510 317.
**OS Grid Ref:** SW 819614.
**Operator:** Lappa Valley Railway Company Ltd.
**Gauge:** 7¼ inch.
**Line Length:** 300 yards, circular.
**First Opened:** c1965.

| No | Name | Type | Builder | Built |
|---|---|---|---|---|
| 6100 | Royal Scot | 4-6-0 | Lilliput Miniature Rlys | 1954 |
| | | 4-4wPH | Mardyke | 1980 |

# MOORS VALLEY RAILWAY

Conceived as a small gauge railway capable of carrying 150,000 passengers per year, the Moors Valley is really in a class of its own. It all started when Roger Marsh built "Tinkerbell", which was the first 7¼ inch gauge locomotive one sat in, rather than on. From this basic theme Jim Haylock has developed the railway's impressive collection of minimum gauge locomotives, capable of hauling heavy trains around the steep gradients and sharp curves of this line, particularly where it spirals around the adventure playground.

When the railway moved here from Tucktonia in 1985, what is now Kingsmere station was the hub of a dairy farm. Now the buildings form a four platform enclosed station, carriage shed, workshop, loco shed and shop. Movements are controlled from two signalboxes, that at Kingsmere having the lever frame formerly installed at Beckton Gas Works in East London. Although basically a circuit, passengers normally travel over the line in two journeys, detraining at Kingsmere whilst the train draws into the headshunt and then back into a departure road. On Sundays only throughout the year a special train, the "Midday Limited" departs for a non-stop run (signals permitting) twice around the circuit, once in each direction. On peak days there is also a shuttle train between Lakeside and Kingsmere stations. Regular special events are held. A 15 inch gauge "Katie" 0-4-2T is under construction here and a 2ft gauge 0-4-0T "Emmet" is kept here between visits to narrow gauge lines.

It might be 7¼ inch gauge, but the Moors Valley is a complete railway in every sense.

**Address:** Moors Valley Country Park, Horton Road, Ashley Heath, Near Ringwood, Dorset, BH24 2ET.
**Telephone:** 01425 471 415.
**OS Grid Ref:** SU 104060.
**Operator:** Narogauge Ltd.
**Website:** www.moorsvalleyrailway.co.uk
**Gauge:** 7¼ inch.
**Line Length:** 1 mile, complex.
**First Opened:** 1986.

| No | Name | Type | Builder | Built |
|---|---|---|---|---|
| (4) | Tinkerbell | 0-4-2T | R Marsh | 1968 |
| 3 | Talos | 0-4-2T | R Marsh | 1978 |
| 6 | Medea | 2-6-2T | J Haylock/M Sharp/J Goss | 1981 |
| (5) | Sapper | 4-6-0 | R Marsh/J Haylock | 1982 |
| 7 | Aelfred | 2-6-4T | Tucktonia | 1985 |
| 9 | Jason | 2-4-4T | Moors Valley Railway | 1989 |
| 10 | Offa | 2-6-2 | Moors Valley Railway | 1991 |
| 11 | Zeus | 2-6-2 | A Culver/Moors Valley Rly | 1991 |
| (14) | Horton | 2-4-0 | Moors Valley Railway | 1991 |
| 12 | Pioneer | 4-6-2 | Moors Valley Railway | 1992 |
| 15 | William Rufus | 2-4-0+0-4-2T | Moors Valley Railway | 1996 |
| | Ivor | 0-4-2T | Crowhurst Engineering | 1997 |

| 16 | Robert Snooks | 0-4-4T | A Manktelow/J Berriman | 1999 |
|----|---------------|--------|------------------------|------|
| 17 | Hartfield | 2-4-4T | M Colbourne | 1999 |
| 19 | Athelstan | 2-8-0 | T Couling | 2006 |
| 18 | Thor | 4-6-2 | A Jefford | 2006 |
| 24 | Perseus | 0-4-2T | P Ash/P Wheeler | 2006 |
| 22 | | 2-4-4T | Moors Valley Railway | U/C |
| 2 | "Horace" | 0-4-2DH | MVR/Roanoke | 1999 |
| | Vixen | 0-4-4-0DH | Moors Valley Railway | 2006 |

# OLD MACDONALD'S FARM MINIATURE RAILWAY

There is one station, from where the train runs round broadly a square shaped track. Although a Wren steam locomotive operated here in the year of opening, motive power has since been petrol powered.

**Address:** Old Macdonald's Farm, Porthcothan Bay, Near Padstow, Cornwall, PL28 8LW.
**Telephone:** 01841 540 829.
**OS Grid Ref:** SW 861711.
**Operator:** J & K Nederpel.
**Website:** www.oldmacdonalds.co.uk
**Gauge:** 7¼ inch.
**Line Length:** 200 yards, circuit.
**First Opened:** 1989.

Site entry fee.

| No | Name | Type | Builder | Built |
|----|------|------|---------|-------|
| | | S/O 4wPH | MRW Railways | 2012 |

▲ 1 "Zebedee" passes 2 "Muffin" on a summer day in 2009 at the Lappa Valley Steam Railway.

**Peter Bryant**

▲ "Eric", named after the railway's founder and built by Alan Keef Ltd, is seen at Newlyn Halt on the Newlyn Branch Line of the Lappa Valley Steam Railway in August 2009.            **Peter Bryant**

▼ 18 "Thor" and 10 "Offa" were built in the workshops of the Moors Valley Railway in Dorset and are seen at the elaborate Kingsmere Station of the same line on 7 October 2011.      **Dave Holroyde**

# PARADISE RAILWAY

A short line in a corner of this bird park with a tunnel, three level crossings and a station.

**Address:** Paradise Park, Hayle, Cornwall, TR27 4HB.
**Telephone:** 01736 751 020.
**OS Grid Ref:** SW 545365.
**Operator:** Paradise Park.
**Website:** www.paradisepark.org.uk
**Gauge:** 15 inch.
**Line Length:** 250 yards, circular.
**First Opened:** 1976.

Park entry fee.

| No | Name | Type | Builder | Built |
|----|------|------|---------|-------|
| 3 | Jungle Express | 4wDM | Lister | 1938 |

# POOLE PARK RAILWAY

A long established line meandering around the lake and through woodland in Poole Park. Since 2007, the line has been considerably upgraded with a new steam locomotive and now sees two train operation at peak times.

**Address:** Poole Park, Parkstone Road, Poole, Dorset, BH15 2SF.
**Telephone:** 07947 846 262.
**OS Grid Ref:** SZ 025912.
**Operator:** C Bullen.
**Website:** www.pooleparktrains.co.uk
**Gauge:** 10¼ inch.
**Line Length:** 650 yards, circular.
**First Opened:** 1949.

| No | Name | Type | Builder | Built |
|----|------|------|---------|-------|
| | George | 0-4-2T | Exmoor Steam Railway | 2010 |
| | "Desmond" | 4-6wDH | Southern Miniature Railways | 1963 |

# PORTERSWICK JUNCTION LIGHT RAILWAY

This is an interesting circuit with bridges, a tunnel and much attention to detail. The line was due to be doubled in length in 2012.

**Address:** Hidden Valley Discovery Park, Tredidon, St Thomas, Launceston, Cornwall, PL15 8SJ.
**Telephone:** 01566 86463.
**OS Grid Ref:** SX 278849.
**Operator:** Hidden Valley Discovery Park.
**Website:** www.hiddenvalleydiscoverypark.co.uk
**Gauge:** 7¼ inch.
**Line Length:** 450 yards, circular.
**First Opened:** 2002.

| No | Name | Type | Builder | Built |
|----|------|------|---------|-------|
| | William | 0-6-0T+T | F Birchall | 2009 |
| 1 | Albert | 0-4-0PH | Roanoke | 1998 |

# RIO GRANDE RAILWAY

This line runs in a country park on the eastern outskirts of Weymouth. The station at Greenhill has two platforms whilst the shed has three roads, accessed from a turntable.

**Address:** Lodmoor Country Park, Weymouth, Dorset, DT4 7SX.
**Telephone:** 01305 785 747.
**OS Grid Ref:** SY 685807.
**Operator:** D Melhuish.
**Website:** www.visitweymouth.co.uk
**Gauge:** 10¼ inch.
**Line Length:** 550 yards, circular.
**First Opened:** 1983.

| No | Name | Type | Builder | Built |
|----|------|------|---------|-------|
| 1890 | | S/O 2-6-0DH | Severn Lamb | 1990 |

# SOUTH DEVON MINIATURE RAILWAY

This railway is located in the gardens at Buckfastleigh Station on the South Devon Railway. There are two routes operating, both around half a mile in length. The journey time, depending on the loco heading the train, is around 8 to 10 minutes and the route runs along the edge of the River Dart taking in views of the gardens of the South Devon Railway as well as picnic areas, engine sheds and other parts of the railway that not all the visitors get to see. Each of the locomotives travels roughly 1,000 miles per year on average, hauling trains consisting of both sit-astride and conventional seating.

**Address:** South Devon Railway Station, Buckfastleigh, Devon, TQ11 0DZ.
**Telephone:** 07040 903 729.
**OS Grid Ref:** SX 747663.
**Operator:** South Devon Miniature Railway Society for South Devon Railway Trust.
**Website:** www.sdmr.me.uk
**Gauge:** 7¼ inch.
**Line Length:** ½ mile with choice of 2 routes.
**First Opened:** 1977.

| No | Name | Type | Builder | Built |
|----|------|------|---------|-------|
| | Tazmin | 0-4-0WT+T | T Carder/G Cooper | 1998 |
| | Sentinel | 6wVBT | D Clayton | 2001 |
| | Rhianna | 0-4-0ST+T | G Cooper | 2006 |
| | | 0-4-0PH | Roanoke | 1998 |
| | | 4w-4wPM | D Renner | |

# WESTON MINIATURE RAILWAY    To close, 9/9/12 + sold

Originally devised by miniature railways expert and published author Robin Butterell, the railway runs from Putters Junction and round the putting green and then along the sea front at the southern end of Weston promenade.

**Address:** Beach Lawns, Marine Parade, Weston Super Mare, Somerset, BS23 1AL.
**Telephone:** 01934 643 510.
**OS Grid Ref:** ST 316600.
**Operator:** R Bullock.
**Website:** www.westonminiaturerailway.co.uk
**Gauge:** 7¼ inch.
**Line Length:** 850 yards, dumb-bell.
**First Opened:** 1981.

| No | Name | Type | Builder | Built |
|----|------|------|---------|-------|
| 1 | Dylan | S/O 4wPH | R Greatrex/R Bullock | 1985 |
| | | S/O 4wBER | Parkside | 2000 |
| 3 | Dennis | 4w-4PH | A Bimpson/R Bullock | 1981 |

▲ This 4-6wDH is the resident diesel workhorse of the Poole Park Railway in Dorset, pictured here on 9 October 2011. Formerly known as "Desmond", it now sports a striking livery reminiscent of a Virgin Pendolino. **Dave Holroyde**

▼ Exmoor Steam Railway built 0-4-2T "George" is seen in use at the Poole Park Railway, passing the locomotive shed spur on 9 October 2011. **Dave Holroyde**

# WOODLAND RAILWAY

The country park covers eighty acres of historic broad leaved woodland, through part of which this line runs, taking passengers to Adventure Land station for the adventure playground. All the structures are constructed from wood, including a substantial embankment and bridge.

**Address:** Brokerswood Country Park, Brokerswood, Westbury, Wiltshire, BA13 4EH.
**Telephone:** 01373 822 238.
**OS Grid Ref:** ST 838524.
**Operator:** Brokerswood Country Park.
**Website:** www.brokerswoodcountrypark.co.uk
**Gauge:** 10¼ inch.
**Line Length:** 600 yards, end to end.
**First Opened:** 1991.

Park entry fee.

| No | Name | Type | Builder | Built |
|---|---|---|---|---|
| | Amelia | 4w-4wDH | Mardyke | 1987 |

▲ 4217 "Black Swan" in steam at the Bentley Miniature Railway, the line of the Uckfield Model Railway Club, on 16 May 2009. **Dave Holroyde**

# AREA 2: SOUTH EAST

Hampshire, Kent, Surrey, Sussex.

## AVON VALLEY NURSERIES RAILWAY

This line was built by the team from the Moors Valley Railway, and is operated at weekends. It runs through the fruit fields then returns via a tunnel. There is also a hand worked 22 inch gauge line here, which crosses the 7¼ inch gauge circuit on the level - an unusual piece of trackwork.

**Address:** Avon Valley Nurseries, South Gorley, Near Fordingbridge, Hampshire, SP6 2PP.
**Telephone:** 01425 650 408.
**OS Grid Ref:** SU 163105.
**Operator:** R Kinnison.
**Gauge:** 7¼ inch.
**Line Length:** 800 yards, circular.
**First Opened:** 1991.

Park entry fee.

| No | Name | Type | Builder | Built |
|----|------|------|---------|-------|
| | Jupiter | 2-4-0 | Moors Valley Railway | 1991 |

▲ LMS Class 4F 4039 "Rachel" is one of the scale steam locomotives in use at the Eastbourne Miniature Steam Railway. GWR 2-8-0 3802 can be seen in the background on 15 September 2009.
**Dave Holroyde**

# BANKSIDE MINIATURE RAILWAY

Among public miniature railways this one is most unusual, featuring raised track of 8¼ inch gauge. The line first ran from end to end on a different site here. It moved to the present site in 1989 and was converted to a balloon loop in 1999. Upon its return the entire train, pulled by "Carolyn", is revolved using a 35 foot diameter turntable. A fascinating location, not to be missed! There are also two 7¼ inch gauge locomotives here, which operate on a 100 yard end to end ground level track.

**Address:** Brambridge Park Garden Centre, Kiln Lane, Brambridge, Winchester, Hampshire, SO50 6HT.
**Telephone:** 07816 773 761 (Evenings).
**OS Grid Ref:** SU 467222.
**Operator:** P Merritt.
**Gauge:** 8¼ inch.
**Line Length:** 300 yards, balloon loop, elevated.
**First Opened:** 1977.

| No | Name | Type | Builder | Built |
|----|------|------|---------|-------|
| 815 | Carolyn | 2-6-2T | | 1924 |
| 2130 | | 0-6-0ST* | J Reynolds | 1994 |
| 1369 | | 0-6-0PT* | J Moody/H Merritt | 2008 |

* 7¼ inch gauge locomotives

# BENTLEY MINIATURE RAILWAY

Quite a notable stud of locomotives is based at this model engineers' track. The line runs from Bentley Central station, along a hedge lined stretch leading to farmland before arriving at Bentley East and the woodland reserve. The line then runs in parallel to the reserve on its return to Glyndebourne Wood station, before diving into a cutting and tunnel and returning through open farmland to Bentley Central station. The circuit is two loops with a long double track section in between.

**Address:** Bentley Wildfowl and Motor Museum, Halland, Near Uckfield, East Sussex, BN8 5AF.
**Telephone:** 01825 840 573.
**OS Grid Ref:** TQ 484159.
**Operator:** Uckfield Model Railway Club.
**Website:** www.bentleyrailway.co.uk
**Gauge:** 5 inch/7¼ inch.
**Line Length:** 1 mile, circular.
**First Opened:** 1985.

Park entry fee.

| No | Name | Type | Builder | Built |
|----|------|------|---------|-------|
| 1466 | | 0-4-2T | W Powell | 1978 |
| | Remus | 0-4-0WT | P Southern | 1981 |
| 44804 | | 4-6-0 | Guest/Rogers | 1984 |
| 8402 | Buffalo | 2-8-0 | Scarrott/Howard | 1989 |
| | Lorna | 2-4-0 | G Billington | 1991 |
| 70000 | Britannia | 4-6-2 | W Powell | 1991 |
| | William I | 0-4-0ST | P Southern | 1991 |
| | William II | 0-4-0 | P Southern | 1992 |
| | Romulus | 0-4-0 | A Lynn | 1993 |
| | Bill Powell | 0-4-0ST | W Powell | 1993 |
| 78064 | Richard Thomas | 2-6-0 | R Stockings | 1993 |
| 4217 | Black Swan | 0-4-2 | Richards Engineering | 1997 |
| | Elaine | 0-4-0ST | M Aplin | 1998 |
| | Jasmine | 0-4-0ST+T | B Miller | 2001 |
| | Apollo | 0-4-2T | P Southern | 2002 |
| | Emma | 0-4-2T | P Southern | 2002 |
| 1401 | | 0-4-2T | J Rottier | 2003 |
| | Basil | 0-4-0ST | B Miller/J Rottier | 2004 |

|  | Rhian | 0-4-0 | B Morgan | 2006 |
| 7 | Tom Rolt | 0-4-2T | J Rottier | 2007 |
|  | Holmside | 0-6-0ST |  | 2008 |
| 6115 | Scots Guardsman | 4-6-0 | J Mills | 2009 |
| 2 | Joshua | 2-4-0 | Maxitrak/Hansford | 2009 |
|  | Desmond | 0-4-0ST | D Beeney |  |
| 4472 | Flying Scotsman | 4-6-2 | S Hills |  |
|  | Taurus | 0-4-0 |  |  |
|  | Cindy | 0-4-2T |  |  |
|  | Lady Helen | 4w-4PE/BER | Uckfield MRC | c1984 |
| E6007 |  | 4w-4wBE | P Heafield | 1986 |
|  | Bulldog Spirit | 0-4-0BE | Compass House | c1994 |
| 15324 |  | 0-6-0BE | Compass House | 1995 |
|  | Rachel | 0-4-0PH | M Appley | c1996 |
|  |  | 0-4-0BE | P Southern | c1997 |
| D5671 |  | 6w-6wBE | Compass House | 1997 |
| 9 | Hunslet | 4wPM |  | 2000 |
|  | Jenny | 4wBE | Compass House | 2003 |
|  |  | 6w-6wBE | Compass House | 2004 |
|  |  | 4w-4wBE | Compass House | 2006 |
|  | Bentley Belle | 5-car BER | Uckfield MRC | 2009 |
| 31271 | Stratford 1840 – 2001 | 6w-6wBE | Compass House | 2010 |
| 21 |  | 4w-4wBE | Compass House | 2010 |
|  | Lewes Castle | 6wBE | T Sanderson/Compass House | 2011 |
|  | (Fowler) | 0-4-0P |  |  |
|  |  | 4w-4wDH | R Wastie |  |
|  |  | 4w-4wDH | R Greatrex | U/C |

# BOLEBROKE CASTLE & LAKES RAILWAY

This line runs around a 3 acre lake and through woodland.

**Address:** Bolebroke Castle, Hartfield, East Sussex, TN7 4JJ.
**Telephone:** 01892 770 061.
**OS Grid Ref:** TQ 476377.
**Operator:** P Hobcraft.
**Website:** www.bolebrokecastle.co.uk
**Gauge:** 7¼ inch.
**Line Length:** 1100 yards, complex.
**First Opened:** 2001.

| No | Name | Type | Builder | Built |
|---|---|---|---|---|
|  | Charles | 0-4-0ST+T | S Bennett | 1983 |
| 35028 | Clan Line | 4-6-2 | Mardyke | c1986 |
| 34051 | Winston Churchill | 4-6-2 | Mardyke | c1986 |
|  | Mountaineer | 2-6-2T+T | D & G Sims | 1991 |
|  | "Timothy" | 0-4-2T | J Stubbs | 1993 |
|  | Linda | 0-4-0ST | P Carr | 1995 |
|  | Lilla | 0-4-0ST+T | M Mckie | 2004 |
|  | Russell | 2-6-2T | W Scott | 2008 |
|  | "Bolebroke Castle" | 0-6-0T | Bickton NG | 2008 |
| 47548 |  | 6w-6wDH | Mardyke | 1989 |
|  | High Peak | 4-4wPH | A Bimpson | 1992 |
|  | Belinda | 4wBE | Maxitrak/Bryant | 1995 |
|  |  | 6wPH | R Greatrex | 1998 |
|  | Doris | 4w-4w-4wBER | H Richards | 1999 |
| 6000 |  | 4w-4wPH | R Greatrex | 2001 |
| 7443 |  | 4w-4wDH | R Greatrex | 2008 |
|  | Punch | 0-6-0PH | Maxitrak |  |
|  |  | 0-4-0BE | Compass House |  |

# DIDDLYS MINIATURE RAILWAY

This line runs round the boating pool at Brooklands, between Worthing and Lancing. A steam loco ran here for a short time; quite extensive earthworks were necessary to get the track onto a level course.

**Address:** Brooklands Pleasure Park, Western Road, East Worthing, West Sussex, BN15 8RR.
**Telephone:** 07967 361 847 (Evenings).
**OS Grid Ref:** TQ 172036.
**Operator:** K McCluskey.
**Website:** www.thediddlys.co.uk
**Gauge:** 10¼ inch.
**Line Length:** 1000 yards, circular.
**First Opened:** 1965.

| No | Name | Type | Builder | Built |
|----|------|------|---------|-------|
|  | Diddly Dum | S/O 4w-4wDH | J Hudell/K McCluskey | 1985 |
|  | Diddly Dee | S/O 4w-4wDH | K McClusky | 2009 |

# EASTBOURNE MINIATURE STEAM RAILWAY

Eastbourne's 1/8th scale miniature railway allows you to travel on replica coaches around Southbourne Lake; ideal for young and old alike. There is a railway style cafe and lineside nature trail on site.

**Address:** Lottbridge Drove, Eastbourne, East Sussex, BN23 6QJ.
**Telephone:** 01323 520 229.
**OS Grid Ref:** TQ 613012.
**Operator:** The Wadey Family.
**Website:** www.emsr.co.uk
**Gauge:** 7¼ inch.
**Line Length:** 900 yards, circular.
**First Opened:** 1992.

| No | Name | Type | Builder | Built |
|----|------|------|---------|-------|
|  |  | 0-4-2T | M Wadey | 1982 |
| 6172 | Royal Green Jackets | 4-6-0 | M Wadey | 1987 |
| 3802 |  | 2-8-0 | A Newbery | 1988 |
| 4039 | Rachel | 0-6-0 | L & D Markwick | 1993 |
| 914 | Eastbourne | 4-4-0 | L & D Markwick | 1998 |
| 5156 | Ayrshire Yeomanry | 4-6-0 | E Holtum/L Peake | 2000 |
| 70000 | Britannia | 4-6-2 | Winson/L Wadey | 2003 |
| 70014 | Iron Duke | 4-6-2 | A Dixon | 2009 |
| 92220 | Evening Star | 2-10-0 | A Dixon | 2010 |
| D7042 | Eastbourne Herald | 4w-4wPE | M Wadey | 1988 |
| D3015 |  | 0-6-0BE | Compass House | 2000 |
| D6700 | Eleventh Duke of Devonshire | 6w-6wPE | L Wadey | 2004 |

# EASTLEIGH LAKESIDE STEAM RAILWAY

Eastleigh Lakeside has recently joined the ranks of Britain's major miniature railways. A substantial new station building has been built at Eastleigh Parkway and a new platform added at Monks Brook Halt. The line was converted from a balloon loop into a dumb-bell during July 1999, when a 10¼ inch gauge rail was also added. There is a 118 yard long tunnel. Periodic special events are held. Bullock locomotive "Silver Jubilee" is currently on long-term loan from Kerr's Miniature Railway in Arbroath.

**Address:** Lakeside Country Park, Wide Lane, Eastleigh, Hampshire, SO50 5PE.
**Telephone:** 023 8061 2020.
**OS Grid Ref:** SU 449175.
**Operator:** Eastleigh Lakeside Railway Ltd.
**Website:** www.steamtrain.co.uk
**Gauge:** 10¼ inch/7¼ inch.
**Line Length:** 1¼ miles, circular.
**First Opened:** 1992.

| No | Name | Type | Builder | Built |
|---|---|---|---|---|
| 1001 | The Monarch | 4-6-2 | H Bullock | 1932 |
| 1002 | The Empress | 4-6-2 | H Bullock | 1933 |
| 2005 | Silver Jubilee | 4-6-2 | H Bullock | 1935 |
| 2006 | Edward VIII | 4-6-2 | H Bullock | 1936 |
| 1908 | Ernest Henry Upton | 4-4-2 | G&SLE | 1937 |
| 6220 | Coronation | 4-6-2 | E Dove | 1946 |
| 4789 | William Baker | 4-4-2* | W Baker | 1947 |
| 70055 | Rob Roy | 4-6-2 | E Dove/R Pullen | 1948 |
| 6100 | Royal Scot | 4-6-0 | Carland Engineering | 1950 |
| 3 | Francis Henry Lloyd | 4-8-4* | G&SLE/Lloyd | 1959 |
| 4498 | Sir Nigel Gresley | 4-6-2 | W Kirkland | 1967 |
| 8 | David Curwen | 2-6-2* | D Curwen | 1972 |
| 7 | Sandy River | 2-4-2 | A Bimpson | 1983 |
| 10 | Sir Arthur Heywood | 2-6-2* | K Williamson | 1984 |
|  | Sgt Murphy | 0-6-0T* | M Marshall | 1990 |
|  | Sanjo | 0-4-0* | S Battle | 1993 |
|  | Taw | 2-6-2T* | J Horsfield | 1999 |
| 932 | Blundells | 4-4-0* | J Moody | 2000 |
| 1A | Saint-Leonard | 0-4-4-0T* | M Marshall | 2001 |
| 850 | Lord Nelson | 4-6-0 | J Moody | 2007 |
| 850 | Lord Nelson | 4-6-0* | J Moody | 2007 |
| 21C1 | Channel Packet | 4-6-2 | J Moody | 2011 |
| 1994 | Eastleigh | 0-4-0+0-4-0DH | ELSR | 1994 |
| 92 | Florence | 0-6-0DH | ELSR | 1999 |
| 3221 | University of Southampton | 4w-4wBE | Southampton University/ELSR | 1999 |

* 7 ¼ inch gauge locomotives

▲ 10¼ inch gauge 70055 Rob Roy is seen returning to Eastleigh Parkway Station after its 1¼ mile journey round the Eastleigh Lakeside Steam Railway on 8 October 2011. **Dave Holroyde**

# EXBURY GARDENS RAILWAY

This line runs through the spectacular 200 acre gardens in the New Forest and there is a halt mid way round.

**Address:** Exbury Gardens, Exbury, Hampshire, SO45 1AZ.
**Telephone:** 023 8089 1203.
**OS Grid Ref:** SU 423006.
**Operator:** Exbury Gardens.
**Website:** www.exbury.co.uk
**Gauge:** 12¼ inch.
**Line Length:** 1¼ miles, complex.
**First Opened:** 2001.

| No | Name | Type | Builder | Built |
|----|------|------|---------|-------|
| | Rosemary | 0-6-2T | Exmoor Steam Railway | 2001 |
| | Naomi | 0-6-2T | Exmoor Steam Railway | 2002 |
| | Mariloo | 2-6-2 | Exmoor Steam Railway | 2008 |
| | Eddy | 4wDH | Hunslet | 1994 |

# FAVERSHAM MINIATURE RAILWAY

This line takes its unusual gauge from a private miniature railway not far away. This is the only public 9 inch gauge railway and runs through the apple orchards here. A loop was completed in 2011 which will make the ride over 1800 yards when opened in 2012. The railway moved here from Norton Ash Garden Centre in 2000. Two of the line's locomotives "Fran" and "Hibbert", are to be rebuilt.

**Address:** Brogdale Horticultural Trust, Brogdale Farm, Faversham, Kent, ME13 8XZ.
**Telephone:** 01795 536 250 (Evenings) or 07563 681 403 (Sundays 11.00 to 4.00pm).
**OS Grid Ref:** TR 006596.
**Operator:** Faversham Miniature Railway Society.
**Website:** www.favershamminiaturerailway.co.uk
**Gauge:** 9 inch.
**Line Length:** 900 yards, complex.
**First Opened:** 2005.

| No | Name | Type | Builder | Built |
|----|------|------|---------|-------|
| 2 | Robin | 4-4-0 | B K Field | 1935 |
| 12 | Pearl | 0-4-2ST | Maxitrak/A Taylor | 2006 |
| 1 | | 2-6-0 | S Beacon/P Reynolds | U/C |
| 4 | | 4w-4PH | Cromar White | c1974 |
| 6 | Fran | 4wPH | Pfeifferbahn | 1979 |
| 8 | Hibbert | 4wPM | R Day | c1982 |
| 14 | Lady Fiona | 4w-4wPH | P Howard/Crowhurst Eng | c1988 |
| 3 | | 4-4wBE | T Smith | 1990 |
| 5 | | 4wPH | Iron Horse | 1990 |
| 10 | Jasmine | 0-6-0PH | Maxitrak | ? |
| 9 | Kirsty | 2-4w-2PH | M Chapman/A Taylor | 2005 |

# GREAT COCKCROW RAILWAY

This is the inspirational home of 1½ inch (to the foot) scale railways in the UK. The stock list represents a cross section of locomotives likely to be on shed, but it's always changing. Trains from Hardwick Central generally operate over either the circuit route through Everglades Junction (several times, in different directions) or climb the hill over a 45 foot viaduct to terminate at Cockcrow Hill. Periodically a double headed "special" covers both routes; tickets may be booked in advance.

Most trains seat only 12 passengers but they run at very frequent intervals. The intensive and highly professional operation is only made possible by strict block working between the three signal boxes. Authentic signalling is a particular feature, and the pace of events inside the boxes has to be seen to be believed.

**Address:** Hardwick Lane, Lyne, Chertsey, Surrey, KT16 0AD.
**Telephone:** 01932 565 474.
**OS Grid Ref:** TQ 027662.
**Operator:** Ian Allan Miniature Railway Supplies Ltd.
**Website:** www.cockcrow.co.uk
**Gauge:** 7¼ inch.
**Line Length:** 2000 yards, complex.
**First Opened:** 1964.

| No | Name | Type | Builder | Built |
|---|---|---|---|---|
| 1239 | | 4-4-0 | Baldwin Bros | 1913 |
| 1947 | Eureka | 4-6-2 | L Shaw | 1926 |
| 1803 | River Itchen | 2-6-0 | A Schwab/J Davis | 1939 |
| 837 | | 4-6-0 | D Curwen | 1947 |
| 73755 | Longmooor | 2-10-0 | J Liversage | 1948 |
| 46245 | City of London | 4-6-2 | W Miller | 1950 |
| 7915 | Mere Hall | 4-6-0 | Rowe | 1952 |
| 206 | | 2-6-0 | D Simmonds | 1956 |
| 1935 | | 2-6-0 | H Saunders | 1974 |
| No.1 | Lulubelle | 0-4-0 | | 1978 |
| 1401 | | 0-4-2T | R Sills | 1980 |
| 5000 | Sister Dora | 4-6-0 | A Glaze | 1981 |
| 2422 | North Foreland | 4-4-2 | J Lester | 1983 |
| 850 | Lord Nelson | 4-6-0 | D Scarrott | 1985 |
| 1249 | Hecate | 0-8-0 | R Sills | 1986 |
| 10 | | 0-6-0ST | Stobbs | 1987 |
| 6115 | Scots Guardsman | 4-6-0 | P Almond | 1988 |
| 1442 | | 4-4-2 | Parkinson/Hammond | 1988 |
| 2744 | Grand Parade | 4-6-2 | R Warren | 1990 |
| 5145 | | 4-6-0 | Axon/Sleet | 1991 |
| 21C11 | General Steam Navigation | 4-6-2 | Lester/Sleet | 1993 |
| 8374 | | 2-8-0 | Glaze/Hancock & York | 1993 |
| 45157 | Glasgow Highlander | 4-6-0 | D Grant | 1997 |
| 30541 | | 0-6-0 | J Butt | 2000 |
| 45440 | | 4-6-0 | J Clarke/N Sleet | 2003 |
| | Alison | 0-4-2T | N Trower | 2006 |
| 70054 | Dornoch Firth | 4-6-2 | K Richardson | U/C |
| 135 | Livvy | S/O 4wBE | M Scrutton | 2008 |
| 7112 | (Winifred) | 0-6-0PM | W Jennings/A B Mcleod | 1958 |
| D9007 | Pinza | 6-6wPH | Mardyke | c1979 |
| D7028 | A.B McLeod | 4w-4wBE | A Glaze | 1982 |
| 60097 | Pillar | 6w-6wBE | N Sleet | 2008 |

# HASTINGS MINIATURE RAILWAY

This line runs from Rock-a-Nore station, where the sheds are located, to Marine Parade Station. After a recent takeover the railway has seen many changes with additional locomotives, new carriages and renovated station areas.

**Address:** Rock-a-Nore Road, Hastings, East Sussex, TN34 3DW.
**Telephone:** 07773 645 228 (Evenings).
**OS Grid Ref:** TQ 827094.
**Operator:** D Radcliffe & D R Miller.
**Gauge:** 10¼ inch.
**Line Length:** 600 yards, end to end.
**First Opened:** 1948.

| No | Name | Type | Builder | Built |
|---|---|---|---|---|
| 3 | Firefly | 0-4-0ST+T | R Yates | 1992 |
| | Swee' Pea | S/O 0-6-0+4wDH | A Keef/RVM | 2012 |
| 5 | Uncle Jim | 4-4wDM | J Hughes | 1968 |
| | Jerry Lee | 4w-4wDH | RVM Engineering | 2011 |
| 4 | Speedy Fizzle | 4w-4wDH | RVM Engineering | 2011 |

▲ Usually resident at the Fairbourne Railway, 4 "Sherpa" is seen here on loan at the Littlehampton Miniature Railway in April 2012.
**John Binch**

# HOLLYCOMBE WORKING STEAM MUSEUM, GARDEN RAILWAY

This small miniature line is an attraction at the magnificent Hollycombe collection, where one can also ride upon a 2 foot gauge line behind the only operational Hunslet Mills class loco; "Jerry M" of 1895, the standard gauge line behind Cockerill Belgian Tram Loco "Yvonne" of 1920, the woodland traction engine ride and enjoy rides on the complete Edwardian Steam Fair and entertainment in the Edwardian Period Bioscope.

**Address:** Iron Hill, Midhurst Road, Liphook, West Sussex, GU30 7LP.
**Telephone:** 01428 724 900.
**OS Grid Ref:** SU 854294.
**Operator:** Hollycombe Working Steam Museum.
**Website:** www.hollycombe.co.uk
**Gauge:** 7¼ inch.
**Line Length:** 400 yards, circular.
**First Opened:** 1982.

Park entry fee.

| No | Name | Type | Builder | Built |
|----|------|------|---------|-------|
| | Bob | 0-4-2T | P Howard | 1981 |
| | Pauline | 0-4-0 | Bennett Bros | 1990 |
| | Tess | 0-4-0ST | D Coupling | 1991 |
| | Lisa | 0-4-0 | G Mullis | 1992 |
| | Jennifer | 0-4-0VBT | R Millard | 1995 |

# HOTHAM PARK MINIATURE RAILWAY

A circuit through woodland in Hotham Park, where the station is situated next to a small amusement park.

**Address:** Hotham Park, Bognor Regis, West Sussex, PO21 1HW.
**Telephone:** 07880 744 597.
**OS Grid Ref:** SZ 939995.
**Operator:** CTS Narrow Gauge Railways LLP.
**Website:** www.hothamparkrailway.co.uk
**Gauge:** 12¼ inch.
**Line Length:** 900 yards, circuit.
**First Opened:** 1969.

| No | Name | Type | Builder | Built |
|----|------|------|---------|-------|
| | Boris | S/O 0-6-0DH | Alan Keef | 2007 |

# LITTLEHAMPTON MINIATURE RAILWAY

This long established line runs from Norfolk Road, on the sea front, to Mewsbrook Park, a public park with boating rides etc. For many years the railway was operated by two 4-6-4s built by John Thurston, who devised the 12¼ inch gauge so as to give more stability than 10¼ inch.

**Address:** Mewsbrook Park, Littlehampton, West Sussex, BN16 2LX.
**Telephone:** 01460 221 303.
**OS Grid Ref:** TQ 042016.
**Operator:** T I R Ltd.
**Website:** www.littlehamptonrailway.co.uk
**Gauge:** 12¼ inch.
**Line Length:** 800 yards, end to end.
**First Opened:** 1948.

| No | Name | Type | Builder | Built |
|----|------|------|---------|-------|
| D1 | | 4w-4wDH | B Whalley | 2007 |

# MARWELL'S WONDERFUL RAILWAY

Marwell Wildlife is world famous for its conservation and breeding of endangered species. The rail train ride gives close up views of some of the animals. Trains run from Treetops Junction on a track with balloon loops at each end to provide an approximate 15 minute non-stop round trip returning to Treetops Junction.

**Address:** Marwell Wildlife, Colden Common, Near Winchester, Hampshire, SO21 1JH.
**Telephone:** 01962 777 407.
**OS Grid Ref:** SU 508216.
**Operator:** Marwell Wildlife.
**Website:** www.marwell.org.uk
**Gauge:** 15 inch.
**Line Length:** 900 yards, dumb-bell.
**First Opened:** 1987.

Site entry fee.

| No | Name | Type | Builder | Built |
|----|------|------|---------|-------|
| | Princess Anne | S/O 2-6-0DH | Severn Lamb | 1987 |

# MID HANTS MINIATURE RAILWAY

This line is situated at Ropley High Level, near the picnic area.

**Address:** Mid Hants Railway (The Watercress Line), Ropley Station, Ropley, Hampshire, SO24 0BL.
**Telephone:** 01962 733 810.
**OS Grid Ref:** SU 630325.
**Operator:** Mid Hants Railway
**Website:** www.watercressline.co.uk
**Gauge:** 10¼ inch.
**Line Length:** 200 yards, end to end.
**First Opened:** 2006.

| No | Name | Type | Builder | Built |
|----|------|------|---------|-------|
| | Pauline | 4-4wDE | G Hunt | |
| | Nevada | 4-4wPH | A Bimpson | 1996 |

# MIZENS RAILWAY

Mizens Railway is the 7¼ inch gauge operation of the Woking Miniature Railway Society. The railway covers a large part of the 10 acre site with about 1½ miles of track. Also to be seen are a number of railway style buildings that cater for both the trains and visitors. The railway opens to the public on Summer Sundays between 14.00 and 17.00 plus for a number of special events. Also to be seen are some interesting full size artefacts including a Dubs Tank Locomotive of 1899 origin and a 4-VEP Driving Trailer from the last regular slam door train to pass through Woking.

**Address:** Woking Miniature Railway Society, Barrs Lane, Knaphill, Woking, Surrey, GU21 2JW.
**Telephone:** 020 8890 1978.
**OS Grid Ref:** SU 967595.
**Operator:** Woking Miniature Railway Society.
**Website:** www.mizensrailway.co.uk
**Gauge:** 7¼ inch.
**Line Length:** 1200 yards, complex.
**First Opened:** 2001.

| No | Name | Type | Builder | Built |
|----|------|------|---------|-------|
| | Marquis | 0-6-0T | L Chandler | 1984 |
| | Richard Bonsey | 0-4-0ST+T | A Chandler | c1984 |
| | Hazel | 0-4-0ST | J Rowland | 1985 |
| 5 | Koala | 2-6-2T | M Rickers | 1990 |
| | Isabel | 0-4-0ST+T | Page Engineering | 1990 |
| | Little John | 2-4-2T | P Beale | 1990 |

▲ Double-headed steam locomotives at the Eastleigh Lakeside Steam Railway. 4498 "Sir Nigel Gresley" and 6220 "Coronation" pause at Monks Brook Halt on 8 October 2011.  **Dave Holroyde**

▼ Perhaps the best-known of all miniature railways is the Romney, Hythe & Dymchurch Railway. Here, 8 "Hurricane" passes under the working signal gantry at the entrance to Hythe station on 12 August 2009.  **Peter Bryant**

| No | Name | Type | Builder | Built |
|---|---|---|---|---|
| 7 | Earl of Maybury | 0-6-0ST | A Chandler | 1991 |
| | Alice | 0-4-0ST+T | D Bradbury | 1996 |
| 8 | Dickwillydan | 0-4-0ST | Mallerby | 1996 |
| 11 | Sir Thomas | 0-4-0ST+T | M Smith | 1996 |
| | Yeo | 2-6-2T | D Bradbury | 2009 |
| 1504 | Paddington | 0-6-0PT | S Conway | c2011 |
| 6 | Sophie | S/O 2-6-0PH | M Rickers | 1995 |
| | Brooklands | 4-4wBE | T Smith | 1978 |
| | Mayflower | 4wBE | Maxitrak | 1985 |
| | Busy Bee | 4wBER | M Rickers | c1986 |
| | Sonya | 0-4-0PH | J Rough | 1996 |
| | Bourne Again | 4wPH | D Bradbury/G Dare | 1996 |
| | | 0-6-0BE | R Dewar | 1997 |
| | Hogwarts School | 0-6-0BE | Compass House | 1997 |
| | RonnyRascal | 6wPH | R Greatrex | 1998 |
| 912 | Goliath | 4w-4wBE | D Bradbury | 2001 |
| | Lemon | 4wPH | Roanoke | 2004 |
| No.18 | | 4-4wBER | G Dare | 2008 |
| | Chestnut | 4wPH | R Scrivenor | 2008 |
| 2006 | Georgia May | 4wBE | Maxitrak | c2009 |
| | Phil Chambers | 4w-4wDH | J Cornell/P Willis | 2009 |

# NEWHAVEN MINIATURE RAILWAY

A simple circuit at the back of this garden/leisure centre. The "Hymek" hauls a set of Mardyke "sit-in" coaches finished in Brighton Belle colours.

**Address:** Paradise Park, Avis Road, Newhaven, East Sussex, BN9 0DH.
**Telephone:** 01273 512 123.
**OS Grid Ref:** TQ 448023.
**Operator:** Paradise Park.
**Website:** www.paradisepark.co.uk
**Gauge:** 7¼ inch.
**Line Length:** 200 yards, circular.
**First Opened:** 1989.

| No | Name | Type | Builder | Built |
|---|---|---|---|---|
| | | 4w-4wDH | Mardyke | 2011 |

# PAULTONS RAILWAY

This Severn Lamb train known at the park as "The Rio Grande Train", is just one of over 60 different attractions at Paultons Park. Trains run clockwise from the station, and alongside Paultons Lake for the last part of the journey.

**Address:** Paultons Family Theme Park, Ower, Romsey, Hampshire, SO51 6AL.
**Telephone:** 023 8081 4442.
**OS Grid Ref:** SU 317167.
**Operator:** Paultons Park Ltd.
**Website:** www.paultonspark.co.uk
**Gauge:** 15 inch.
**Line Length:** 700 yards, circular.
**First Opened:** 1987.

Park entry fee.

| No | Name | Type | Builder | Built |
|---|---|---|---|---|
| | | S/O 2-8-0DH | Severn-Lamb | 1986 |

# ROMNEY, HYTHE & DYMCHURCH RAILWAY

The RH&DR is probably the best known miniature railway in the world. It is a complete railway system in miniature with comprehensive construction and maintenance facilities. There are six stations, eleven steam locomotives, two passenger diesels and three small internal combustion powered engines for permanent way work. Passenger coaches (over sixty in number) include a licensed "Bar Car" which is the longest vehicle built to run on 15 inch gauge. The section between Hythe and New Romney is double track.

**Address:** New Romney, Kent, TN28 8PL.
**Telephone:** 01797 362 353.
**OS Grid Ref:** TR 153347 (Hythe).
**Operator:** The Romney, Hythe & Dymchurch Light Railway Co Ltd.
**Website:** www.rhdr.co.uk
**Gauge:** 15 inch.
**Line Length:** 14 miles.
**First Opened:** 1927.

| No | Name | Type | Builder | Built |
|---|---|---|---|---|
| 1 | Green Goddess | 4-6-2 | Davey Paxman | 1925 |
| 2 | Northern Chief | 4-6-2 | Davey Paxman | 1925 |
| 3 | Southern Maid | 4-6-2 | Davey Paxman | 1926 |
| 4 | The Bug | 0-4-0 | Krauss | 1926 |
| 5 | Hercules | 4-8-2 | Davey Paxman | 1926 |
| 6 | Samson | 4-8-2 | Davey Paxman | 1926 |
| 7 | Typhoon | 4-6-2 | Davey Paxman | 1926 |
| 8 | Hurricane | 4-6-2 | Davey Paxman | 1926 |
| 9 | Winston Churchill | 4-6-2 | Yorkshire Engine | 1931 |
| 10 | Doctor Syn | 4-6-2 | Yorkshire Engine | 1931 |
| 11 | Black Prince | 4-6-2 | Krupp | 1937 |
| 4 | | 4wDM | Motor Rail | 1938 |
| (PW2) | Scooter | 2w-2PM | RH&DR | 1949 |
| (PW3) | Redgauntlet | 4wPM | Jacot/Keef | 1977 |
| 12 | John Southland | 4w-4wDH | TMA Engineering | 1983 |
| 14 | Captain Howey | 4w-4wDH | TMA Engineering | 1989 |

# ROYAL VICTORIA RAILWAY

This line uses part of the trackbed of an earlier 10¼ inch gauge railway, but is far more ambitious than its predecessor. A further steam locomotive is under construction. A terminus station, carriage shed/tunnel, and a further ½ mile of track was due to be completed by Spring 2012. The Binning locomotive here is to have a major rebuild.

**Address:** Royal Victoria Country Park, Netley, Southampton, Hampshire, SO31 5GA.
**Telephone:** 023 8045 6246.
**OS Grid Ref:** SU 464079.
**Operator:** P Bowers.
**Website:** www.royalvictoriarailway.co.uk
**Gauge:** 10¼ inch.
**Line Length:** 1000 yards, circular.
**First Opened:** 1996.

| No | Name | Type | Builder | Built |
|---|---|---|---|---|
| 46100 | Royal Scot | 4-6-0 | Bassett Lowke | 1938 |
| 2 | Basil the Brigadier | 2-6-0+0-6-2 | Kitson | 1938 |
| 3 | Trevithick | 0-6-2T | R Marsh | 1975 |
| 4 | Isambard Kingdom Brunel | 2-6-0 | D Curwen | 1977 |
| 5 | Peter the Private | 2-6-0 | P Bowers/D Curwen | U/C |
| D1011 | Western Thunderer | 6w-6PM | D Curwen | 1964 |
| D1000 | Western Independence | 6w-6wDH | D Curwen | 1964 |
| D1002 | Western Explorer | 6w-6wDH | Severn Lamb | 1967 |
| 6 | HST 125 | 4w-4w | A Binning | 1988 |
| 1 | Maurice the Major | 4w-4wDH | P Bowers | 1996 |

# SOUTH DOWNS LIGHT RAILWAY

The line in its current gauge has been in existence since 2000, although there was a 7¼ inch gauge line here previously. The railway was extended to its current length for the 2006 season, with a station building and three-road engine shed and workshop constructed. The route features a deep cutting.

**Address:** Pulborough Garden Centre, Stopham Road, Pulborough, West Sussex, RH20 1DS.
**Telephone:** 07518 753 784.
**OS Grid Ref:** TQ 033183.
**Operator:** South Downs Light Railway Society.
**Website:** www.sdlrs.com
**Gauge:** 10¼ inch.
**Line Length:** 1100 yards, circular.
**First Opened:** 2000.

| No | Name | Type | Builder | Built |
|---|---|---|---|---|
| 4472 | Flying Scotsman | 4-6-2 | J J Mahoney | 1935 |
| 46100 | Royal Scot | 4-6-0 | A Gutzewitz | c1973 |
| | Arthur | 0-6-0ST | J Hudell | 1982 |
| 13245 | | 2-6-0 | P Howard/Crowhurst Eng | 1988 |
| 771 | Sir Sagramore | 4-6-0 | Richards Eng/P Howard | 1994 |
| 1 | Alice | 0-4-2ST+T | G Favell | 2001 |
| 319 | Pulborough | 0-4-2T | Exmoor Steam Railway | 2004 |
| 334 | Peggy | 0-4-2T | Exmoor Steam Railway | 2007 |
| | Tinkerbell | 4wPM | Coleby Simkins | 1971 |
| D7062 | Arctic Prince | 4w-4wDH | Mardyke | 1982 |
| | Merlin | 0-4-0DH | Roanoke | 2004 |

▲ Built in 1975, 3 "Trevithick" was the first 10¼ inch gauge locomotive to have a closed cab. It now operates at the Royal Victoria Railway, and is seen here on 7 October 2011. **Dave Holroyde**

# STANSTED PARK LIGHT RAILWAY

The line runs through the grounds of the park and the main station is at the bottom of the garden centre car park. Features include a bridge over a pond and track through an arboretum and ancient woodland.

**Address:** Stansted House, Rowlands Castle, West Sussex, P09 6DX.
**Telephone:** 01243 670 724 (Evenings).
**OS Grid Ref:** SU 759100.
**Operator:** G Jago.
**Website:** www.splr.info
**Gauge:** 7¼ inch.
**Line Length:** 850 yards, circular.
**First Opened:** 2005.

| No | Name | Type | Builder | Built |
|---|---|---|---|---|
| | Ladybird | 2-6-4T | F Kenny | 1992 |
| 4 | | 0-4-4T | E Walker | 2001 |
| | Cheyanne | 2-8-0 | G Jago | 2002 |
| | Ludwig | 0-6-0 | F Birchall | 2005 |
| | Grafter | 0-4-0PH | Roanoke | 2003 |
| 5 | Ted | 0-6-0PH | Pfeifferbahn/G Campbell | c2004 |
| | | 4wPH | L A Services | |

# STRAND PARK MINIATURE RAILWAY

A simple line from Apache station around the Lido on the sea front at Gillingham. There is one station, a tunnel, and a loop.

**Address:** Strand Leisure Park, Gillingham, Kent, ME7 1TT.
**Telephone:** 01634 852 907.
**OS Grid Ref:** TQ 785693.
**Operator:** Medway Council (Black Lion Leisure).
**Website:** www.medway.gov.uk
**Gauge:** 7¼ inch.
**Line Length:** 400 yards, circular.
**First Opened:** c1951.

| No | Name | Type | Builder | Built |
|---|---|---|---|---|
| 112 | | 4w-4wDH | Mardyke | 1987 |

# SWANLEY NEW BARN RAILWAY

Trains depart from Lakeside station, which is a four-road, three platform station, around an extended loop to New Barn Halt which is adjacent to the main car park, and returns via the other side of the park. This line features intricate signalling; its lever frame previously saw service with London Underground. Lakeside station is adjacent to the main park activities, and the railway runs as a miniature commuter line conveying passengers and their luggage to main area, and leads to rush hour type services on busy days as everyone heads home at a similar time. Locomotives under construction and expected in service over the next five years are a DMU, two or three "Tinkerbell" 0-4-2T steam locomotives, and two new diesels from Mardyke Miniature Railways.

**Address:** Swanley Park, New Barn Road, Swanley, Kent, BR8 7PW.
**OS Grid Ref:** TQ 515696.
**Operator:** Swanley New Barn Railway.
**Website:** www.snbr.co.uk
**Gauge:** 7¼ inch.
**Line Length:** 900 yards, balloon.
**First Opened:** 1986.

| No | Name | Type | Builder | Built |
|---|---|---|---|---|
| 1 | Sir Goss | 2-4-0 | J Goss | 1981 |
| 1 | Lady Sara/Furbero | 0-4-0T+T | J Drury | 1984 |
| 3 | Romulus | 0-4-0T+T | P Beale | 1988 |

| | Owd Rosie | 2-6-2T | J Stubbs | 1992 |
|---|---|---|---|---|
| 414 | Montezuma | 2-8-0 | J Stubbs | 1994 |
| 4468 | Mallard | 4-6-2 | Mardyke | 2000 |
| | Siusaidh | 2-4-4T | P Beevers | 2008 |
| | Prince Sheian | 2-4-0 | P Jackson | 2010 |
| | Zebedee | 0-4-2T | P Beevers | 2012 |
| | Red Rum | 4w-4BE | Pfeifferbahn | 1986 |
| CC40101 | | 6w-6wDH | Mardyke | 1987 |
| D9015 | Tulyar | 6w-6wDH | Mardyke | 1987 |
| D7612 | Steptoe | 4w-4wPH | E Ward | 1988 |
| (D7076) | | 4w-4wDH | Mardyke | 1989 |
| 47845 | County of Kent | 6w-6wDH | Mardyke | 1992 |
| | Yellow Peril | 2w-2BE | E Ward | 1998 |
| HS4000 | Kestrel | 6w-6wDH | Mardyke | 1999 |
| | Tegen | 4wDH | J Deans | 2000 |
| | Skipper | 4wDH | P Beevers | 2011 |
| | Nipa | 4wDH | P Jackson/N Dove | 2012 |
| D1000 | Western Enterprise | 6w-6wDH | Mardyke | 2012 |

## WELLINGTON COUNTRY PARK RAILWAY

This line has been changed from a balloon loop to a circuit. Trains pass through a tunnel and over a pond on their way back to the station. There is a fair sized shed accessed via a turntable.

**Address:** Wellington Country Park, Riseley, Near Heckfield, Hampshire, RG7 1SP.
**Telephone:** 0118 932 6444.
**OS Grid Ref:** SU 730627.
**Operator:** Wellington Country Park.
**Website:** www.wellington-country-park.co.uk
**Gauge:** 7¼ inch.
**Line Length:** 500 yards, circular.
**First Opened:** 1980.

Park entry fee.

| No | Name | Type | Builder | Built |
|---|---|---|---|---|
| | Charlotte | 0-4-0+0-4-0DH | Crowhurst Eng | 1990 |
| | | 4wBE | Maxitrak | 2008 |

# AREA 3: HOME COUNTIES

Bedfordshire, Berkshire, Buckinghamshire, Greater London, Hertfordshire, Northamptonshire, Oxfordshire.

## BARKING PARK LIGHT RAILWAY

This line runs between Park Gates station and Lakeside Halt, on a virtually straight alignment. The locomotives run round their trains at each end. The line here was previously 9½ inch gauge, and went through a transformation during the 2008/09 winter season under new ownership.

**Address:** Barking Park, Longbridge Road, Barking, London, IG11 8TA.
**Telephone:** 07740 343 801.
**OS Grid Ref:** TQ 446849.
**Operator:** R Armstead.
**Website:** www.bplr.co.uk
**Gauge:** 7¼ inch.
**Line Length:** 350 yards, end to end.
**First Opened:** 1946.

| No | Name | Type | Builder | Built |
|---|---|---|---|---|
| | Drewry | 4wBE | M Coote | 2005 |
| D8234 | | 4w-4wBE | R Armstead/M Coote/MEP | 2008 |
| | Gnat | 4wDH | P Beevers | 2009 |
| | Jack | 4wDH | P Beevers | 2011 |

▲ 4w-4wDH "Elli-Chi" passes the Bird Walk at the Beale Railway in Pangbourne on 11 May 2012.
**John Binch**

# BEALE RAILWAY

Between 1989 and 1994 a 7¼ inch gauge railway operated around this bird park. Now 10¼ inch gauge tracks have been laid, largely following the earlier line's alignment. Trains depart from Howard's Halt and run round the west loop anticlockwise, then run round the east loop clockwise. "Sir Humphry Davy" is ex-Shillingstone Light Railway.

**Address:** Beale Park, Lower Basildon, Pangbourne, Berkshire, RG8 9NH.
**Telephone:** 08707 777 160.
**OS Grid Ref:** SU 618782.
**Operator:** J Treble-Parker.
**Website:** www.bealepark.co.uk
**Gauge:** 10¼ inch.
**Line Length:** 1000 yards, dumb-bell.
**First Opened:** 1989.

Park entry fee

| No | Name | Type | Builder | Built |
|----|------|------|---------|-------|
| | John-Remy | 0-6-2T | Exmoor Steam Railway | 1991 |
| | Sir Humphry Davy | 4w-4wDH | G&SLE | 1960 |
| | Elli-Che | 4w-4wDH | J Treble-Parker | 2007 |

# BEKONSCOT LIGHT RAILWAY

A short line which winds its way behind the famous model village and its Gauge 1 model railway.

**Address:** Bekonscot Model Village, Warwick Road, Beaconsfield, Buckinghamshire, HP9 2PL.
**Telephone:** 01494 672 919.
**OS Grid Ref:** SU 939914.
**Operator:** Bekonscot Model Village.
**Website:** www.bekonscot.co.uk
**Gauge:** 7¼ inch.
**Line Length:** 200 yards, complex.
**First Opened:** 2001.

| No | Name | Type | Builder | Built |
|----|------|------|---------|-------|
| 1 | Sprocket | 4wBE | Maxitrak | 2001 |
| 3 | | 4w-4wBER | Bekonscot | 2001 |
| 5 | Bouncer | 4w-4wBE | Bekonscot | 2007 |
| 6 | Doodargh | 4w-4wDH | Bekonscot | 2010 |

# BILLING AQUADROME RAILWAY

A circuit around one of the lakes in the holiday park alongside the River Nene. There were previously 10¼ inch and 2 foot gauge railways on site, the latter following a similar alignment to the present day line.

**Address:** Billing Aquadrome Holiday Park, Crow Lane, Billing, Northampshire, NN3 9DA.
**Telephone:** 01604 408 181.
**OS Grid Ref:** SP 810614.
**Operator:** Billing Aquadrome.
**Website:** www.billingaquadrome.com
**Gauge:** 15 inch.
**Line Length:** 1000 yards, circuit.
**First Opened:** 2010.

| No | Name | Type | Builder | Built |
|----|------|------|---------|-------|
| 362 | | S/O 2-8-0DH | Severn Lamb | 1978 |

# BLENHEIM PARK RAILWAY

This line performs a useful transport function, carrying visitors from the Palace entrance to the Pleasure Gardens. On peak days the train will be full as soon as the loco has run round, and then it will be off for its next trip. "Anna" is the standby locomotive here and not on public view.

**Address:** Blenheim Palace, Woodstock, Oxfordshire, OX20 1PX.
**Telephone:** 0800 849 6500.
**OS Grid Ref:** SP 443162.
**Operator:** Blenheim Estate.
**Website:** www.blenheimpalace.com
**Gauge:** 15 inch.
**Line Length:** 1000 yards, end to end.
**First Opened:** 1975.

Park entry fee

| No | Name | Type | Builder | Built |
|----|------|------|---------|-------|
| | Sir Winston Churchill | S/O 0-6-2DH | Alan Keef | 1992 |
| | Anna | 4-6wDM | G&SLE | 1960 |

# BROCKWELL PARK MINIATURE RAILWAY

A short end to end line in this popular local park.

**Address:** Brockwell Park, Herne Hill, London, SE24 0PA.
**Telephone:** 07973 613 515.
**OS Grid Ref:** TQ 318743.
**Operator:** J Roberts.
**Website:** www.travelbpmr.com
**Gauge:** 7¼ inch.
**Line Length:** 240 yards, end to end.
**First Opened:** 2003.

| No | Name | Type | Builder | Built |
|----|------|------|---------|-------|
| 2 | Oscar | 2-4-0 | Maxitrak/A Roberts | 2008 |
| | HMS Pembroke | 4-4wPH | Mardkye | c1980 |
| D3014 | The Brockwell Flyer | 0-6-0BE | MEP/J Roberts | 2005 |
| | | 4wBE | Phoenix Locos/J Roberts | 2010 |

# DINOSAUR WOODLAND RAILWAY

The sit-in steam outline locomotives haul two coaches around a circuit in part of the wildlife park. There is one station and a tunnel.

**Address:** Paradise Wildlife Park, White Stubbs Lane, Broxbourne, Hertfordshire, EN10 7QA.
**Telephone:** 01992 470 490.
**OS Grid Ref:** TL 338068.
**Operator:** Paradise Wildlife Park.
**Website:** www.pwpark.com
**Gauge:** 10¼ inch.
**Line Length:** 300 yards, circular.
**First Opened:** c1981.

Park entry fee

| No | Name | Type | Builder | Built |
|----|------|------|---------|-------|
| 6 | | S/O 2-4w-2DM | Shepperton Metal Products | c1971 |
| 1 | | S/O 2-4w-2DH | Paradise Wildlife Park | c1998 |

# EAST HERTS MINIATURE RAILWAY

This line has two circuits, one inside the other, linked by a diamond crossover. The outer line includes a tunnel, whilst the inner one passes over a bridge over a pond.

**Address:** Van Hage Garden Centre, Amwell Hill, Great Amwell, Hertfordshire, SG12 9RP.
**Telephone:** 01920 870 811.
**OS Grid Ref:** TL 367124.
**Operator:** East Herts Miniature Railway Society.
**Website:** www.ehmr.org.uk
**Gauge:** 7¼ inch.
**Line Length:** 440 yards, complex.
**First Opened:** 1978.

| No | Name | Type | Builder | Built |
|----|------|------|---------|-------|
| | T C B Miller | 0-4-2T | A Robelou | 1991 |
| | Peter N Brown | 0-4-2T | Robelou/Carroll | 1994 |
| 12 | Alice | 2-4-2 | J Stubbs | 1996 |
| | Ellan Bee | 0-4-2T | Barber/Cormick | 1997 |
| | John A Patten | 2-6w-2PH | Barnard/Patten/Brown | 1991 |
| | H G Harrison | 0-4-0PH | Roanoke | 1999 |
| | Tug | 0-4-0PH | A Robelou | c2005 |
| | | 0-6-0BE | B Moretti | 2008 |

▲ 5 "Bouncer" is seen in use at the cleverly laid-out Bekonscot Light Railway in 2010, winding its way around the model lake.
**Peter Bryant**

# FANCOTT MINIATURE RAILWAY

Trains run from the terminus at Fancott around a long balloon loop. The railway now has a triangle junction that allows the locomotives and rolling stock to be turned after each journey.

**Address:** Fancott Arms Public House, Fancott, Near Toddington, Bedfordshire, LU5 6HT.
**Telephone:** 07917 756 237.
**OS Grid Ref:** TL 022278.
**Operator:** R Stanbridge.
**Website:** www.fancottrailway.co.uk
**Gauge:** 7¼ inch.
**Line Length:** 585 yards, complex.
**First Opened:** 1996.

| No | Name | Type | Builder | Built |
|---|---|---|---|---|
| | Herbie | 4w-4DH | Severn Lamb | 1984 |
| 47586 | | 4w-4PH | N Atkin | 1992 |
| | Pippa | 4wPH | P Whitmore | 1994 |
| 3 | River Fal | 4wBE | Express Locos/R Wilson | 2003 |

# GOLDING SPRING MINIATURE RAILWAY

This line is located within the Buckinghamshire Railway Centre, adjacent to the standard gauge demonstration track in the "up yard". Trains run from Golding Spring Central station.

**Address:** Buckinghamshire Railway Centre, Quainton Road Station, Station Road, Quainton, Buckinghamshire, HP22 4BY.
**Telephone:** 01296 655 720.
**OS Grid Ref:** SP 741189.
**Operator:** Vale of Aylesbury Model Engineering Society.
**Website:** www.vames.co.uk
**Gauge:** 5 inch/7¼ inch.
**Line Length:** 1100 yards, complex.
**First Opened:** 1982.

Site entry fee

| No | Name | Type | Builder | Built |
|---|---|---|---|---|
| | Catherine | 0-4-0ST+T | J Horsfield | 1982 |
| | Pipit | 0-4-0ST | P Booth | 1992 |
| | Calshot | 0-4-0WT+T | E Faber | 1994 |
| | Curlew | 0-4-0ST+T | R Weeks | 1994 |
| | Bridget | 0-4-2T | E Goodchild | c1994 |
| | Lyn | 0-6-0T | R Urquhart | c1995 |
| 3 | John Pope | 0-4-0T | J Pope | c1995 |
| | Kinnel | 0-6-0T | R Urquhart | 1997 |
| | Champion | 0-4-0ST+T | E Goodchild | 2001 |
| 5 | Lilla | 0-6-2T+T | M Hutt | c2001 |
| 3 | Best Mate | 0-4-2ST+T | M Hutt | 2005 |
| DS2 | Grasshopper | 0-4-0ST+T | A Gelson | 2009 |
| | (Agenoria) | 0-4-0 | M Bidmead | 2009 |
| 9 | Nutty | 2-8-0 | M Hutt | 2009 |
| DS1 | Flypip | 0-4-0ST+T | | |
| | | 4wBE | R Tyler | 1983 |
| 15103 | | 0-6-0BE | M Potter | 1995 |
| D5909 | | 4w-4wBE | Vale of Aylesbury MES | c1995 |
| | | 2w-2wBER | S Hughes | 2000 |
| | | 4wPE | R Hall | 2004 |
| 3 | | 4w-4wTG | M Bidmead | 2005 |
| (D7091) | | 4w-4PM | D Hill | |

▲ A "Hymek" locomotive waits between duties at Golding Spring Central Station on 5 June 2010.

Dave Holroyde

# GULLIVER'S RAILROAD

A 600 yard circuit at this children's theme park. Trains call at four stations at Main Street, Liliput Land, Adventure Land, and Discovery Bay, where there is a stock siding.

**Address:** Gulliver's Milton Keynes, Livingstone Drive, Newlands, Milton Keynes, Buckinghamshire, MK15 0DT.
**Telephone:** 01925 444 888.
**OS Grid Ref:** SP 872399.
**Operator:** Phillips Family.
**Website:** www.gulliversfun.co.uk
**Gauge:** 15 inch.
**Line Length:** 600 yards, circular.
**First Opened:** 1999.

Park entry fee

| No | Name | Type | Builder | Built |
|----|------|------|---------|-------|
| 2 | | S/O 0-6-0+6wDE | Gulliver's Land | 1999 |

# HARROW & WEMBLEY SOCIETY OF MODEL ENGINEERS

HWSME have a permanent ground level multi-gauge track network, consisting of 3½, 5 and 7¼ inch gauge and a continuous run. The minimum curve radius is 16.5 m (54 ft). The length is 366 m (1200 ft) continuous or 692 m (2270 ft) out and back to terminus. The Roxbourne Park Railway as it is formally known, is open for rides on every Sunday afternoon during British Summer Time from around 14.30 to 17.00, weather and conditions permitting.

**Address:** Roxbourne Park, Field End Road, Eastcote, Harrow, London, HA4 9PB.
**Telephone:** 020 8953 0098.
**OS Grid Ref:** TQ 117868.
**Operator:** Harrow & Wembley Society of Model Engineers.
**Website:** www.hwsme.org.uk
**Gauge:** 3½ inch/5 inch/7¼ inch.
**Line Length:** 700 yards, complex.
**First Opened:** 1976.

| No | Name | Type | Builder | Built |
|----|------|------|---------|-------|
| 5401 | Sir Cumference | 4-6-0 | P Beale | 1982 |
| | Jenny | 0-4-0ST | J Cousins | c1984 |
| 73082 | Camelot | 4-6-0 | J Cousins | 2001 |
| | St George | 0-4-0T+T | A Riches | 2004 |
| 60052 | Prince Palatine | 4-6-2 | J Sarney | c2006 |
| | Bubbles | 0-4-0T | S Mould | 2008 |
| 70007 | Coeur-de-Lion | 4-6-2 | Winson/J Sarney | 2009 |
| D3148 | Tony Baker 1934 - 1999 | 0-6-0BE | D Jeavons | 1998 |
| | | 0-4-0BE | J Cousins | |

# KNEBWORTH PARK MINIATURE RAILWAY   *Closed -/-/12*

This line runs through the grounds of Knebworth Park, adjacent to the car access to Knebworth House. The station is at the top of a short balloon loop, from where the line wends its way down before crossing to the opposite hillside. Like two of the locomotives here, five of the coaches here also derive from Ian Allan Ltd's foray into miniature railway supplies.

**Address:** Knebworth House Gardens and Park, Near Stevenage, Hertfordshire, SG3 6PY.
**Telephone:** 01438 812 661.
**OS Grid Ref:** TL 234215.
**Operator:** Scenic Railways Ltd.
**Website:** www.knebworthhouse.com/visit/railway.html
**Gauge:** 10¼ inch.
**Line Length:** 700 yards, dumb-bell.
**First Opened:** 1991. *Originally opened 1971 on 2'g*

Site entry fee

| No | Name | Type | Builder | Built |
|----|------|------|---------|-------|
| | Edmund Hannay | 0-4-2WT+T | D King | 1972 |
| | Pilgrim | 0-6-0T | D King | 1981 |
| | Hasty | S/O 4w-4wPH | RVM Engineering | 2012 |
| D801 | Jungle Express | 4-4wPM | G&SLE/Paignton Zoo | 1943 |
| | Meteor V | 2-4w-2PM | Shepperton Metal Products | 1970 |
| | Rhuddlan Castle | 4w-4wDH | Fenlow | 1972 |
| | John Glenn | 4wPM | Cocks/Fairweather | 1994 |
| | Midget | 4wPM | Fairweather/Madgin | 2001 |

## MILTON KEYNES MODEL ENGINEERING SOCIETY

The society track used to be at Kingfisher County Club in nearby Deanshanger. They moved from that site and built the elevated multi-gauge track here first, followed by the ground level track in 2010. The club tracks are run every Sunday from 13.00-17.00 April–October, one Saturday a month, all bank holidays and every Friday in the school holidays. Tracks include raised and ground level.

**Address:** Milton Keynes Light Railway, Caldecotte Lake, Bletcham Way, Milton Keynes, Bucks, MK7 8HP.
**Telephone:** 01908 542 671.
**OS Grid Ref:** SP 887355.
**Operator:** Milton Keynes Light Railway.
**Website:** www.mklightrailway.co.uk
**Gauge:** 5 inch/7¼ inch.
**Line Length:** 250 yards, complex.
**First Opened:** 2010.

| No | Name | Type | Builder | Built |
|----|------|------|---------|-------|
| | Edgar | 0-4-0T | | c1991 |
| | Romulus | 0-4-0 | Page Engineering | 1992 |
| 9 | Nutty | 2-8-0 | M Hutt | 2009 |
| 8 | Katie | 6wPH | M Hutt | 2008 |
| | Hilda | 0-4-4-0BE | C Conell | 2012 |
| | Hagrid | 0-4-2PH | | |

## MORTOCOMBE MINIATURE RAILWAY

An unusual dual gauge track in a popular garden centre near Oxford.

**Address:** County Gardens Garden Centre, Newbury Road, Chilton, Near Didcot, Oxfordshire, OX11 1QN.
**Telephone:** 01235 833 900.
**OS Grid Ref:** SU 486860.
**Operator:** Mortocombe Railway Society Ltd.
**Gauge:** 7¼ inch/10¼ inch.
**Line Length:** 300 yards, complex.
**First Opened:** 2005.

| No | Name | Type | Builder | Built |
|----|------|------|---------|-------|
| | Meacanopis | 0-4-2T | J Stubbs | 1991 |
| | Phalaenopsis | 2-4-2T* | Exmoor Steam Railway | 2008 |
| 6643 | | 4-4wPH | R Greatrex | 1993 |
| 6644 | | 4-4wPH | R Greatrex | 2003 |
| | | 4w-4wDH* | Mortocombe MR | U/C |

*10¼ inch gauge

# RUISLIP LIDO RAILWAY

This line has improved beyond recognition since being taken over by volunteers in 1979. Trains now run from the original station at Woody Bay, through the loop at Eleanor's to Haste Hill, then over the latest extension to Ruislip Lido Station. Movements are controlled by radio from the signal box at Woody Bay. The steam locomotive is oil fired so as to avoid lineside fires. Although run wholly by volunteers, the line is maintained and operated to the highest professional standards.

**Address:** Ruislip Lido, Reservoir Road, Ruislip, Hillingdon, London, HA4 7TY.
**Telephone:** 01895 622 595.
**OS Grid Ref:** TQ 089889.
**Operator:** Ruislip Lido Railway Society Ltd.
**Website:** www.ruisliplidorailway.org
**Gauge:** 12 inch.
**Line Length:** 1¼ miles, balloon loop.
**First Opened:** 1945.

| No | Name | Type | Builder | Built |
|---|---|---|---|---|
| 6 | Mad Bess | 2-4-0ST | RLR/Winson Engineering | 1998 |
| 3 | Robert | 4w-4DH | Severn Lamb | 1973 |
| 5 | Lady of the Lakes | 4w-4wDH | Ravenglass & Eskdale Rly | 1986 |
| 7 | Graham Alexander | 4w-4wDH | Severn Lamb | 1990 |
| 8 | Bayhurst | 4w-4wDH | Severn Lamb | 2003 |
| 9 | John Rennie | 4w-4wDM | Severn Lamb | 2004 |

▲ 7 "Graham Alexander" stands at the Ruislip Lido Railway on 17 August 2007.          **Chris Cobley**

# VANSTONE WOODLAND RAILWAY

The track here is basically a circuit, but with the station on a siding from which the train is propelled at the start of each run. The wooded section of the line includes some steep gradients.

**Address:** Vanstone Park Garden Centre, Hitchin Road, Codicote, Near Hitchin, Hertfordshire, SG4 8TH.
**Telephone:** 01438 820 412.
**OS Grid Ref:** TL 213200.
**Operator:** Scenic Railways Ltd.
**Website:** www.vanstonerailway.co.uk
**Gauge:** 10¼ inch.
**Line Length:** 550 yards, balloon loop.
**First Opened:** 1986.

| No | Name | Type | Builder | Built |
|----|------|------|---------|-------|
|  | Borough of Buxton | 2-4w-2DM | Shepperton Metal Products | 1968 |
|  | Sandham Castle | 2-4w-2DM | Shepperton Metal Products | 1969 |
|  | Meteor IV | 2-4w-2DM | Shepperton Metal Products | 1969 |
|  | Meteor IX | 2-4w-2DM | Shepperton Metal Products | c1971 |

# WATFORD MINIATURE RAILWAY

This busy line has its station adjacent to the paddling pool/playground area in Cassiobury Park. Passengers ride over a gated crossing and then round upon themselves in an area adjacent to the River Gade, a total journey of 1020 yards. "Marri" is a very powerful machine which was built in Australia and imported especially for use here; it has an unusual "Briggs" firebox. At peak times operation here can be very slick indeed. Other locomotives visit occasionally.

**Address:** Cassiobury Park, Watford, Hertfordshire, WD18 7LG.
**OS Grid Ref:** TQ 090972.
**Operator:** J Price.
**Gauge:** 10¼ inch.
**Line Length:** 600 yards, complex.
**First Opened:** 1959.

| No | Name | Type | Builder | Built |
|----|------|------|---------|-------|
| 4179 | Chiltern Shuttle | 0-6-0 | R Morse | 1946 |
|  | Nelly | 2-4-0ST+T | Richards Engineering | 1977 |
| 7 | Marri | 2-6-0 | Willis Light Engineering | 1993 |
|  |  | S/O 0-6-0DH | Roanoke | 2005 |
|  | Conway Castle | 4w-4wDH | Fenlow | 1972 |
|  | Nikki Louise | 0-6-0DH | R Prime | 1988 |

# WILLEN LAKE MINIATURE RAILWAY

A there-and-back line in a corner of this large public park, popular for its watersports facilities.

**Address:** Willen Lakeside Park, Milton Keynes, Buckinghamshire, MK15 0DS.
**Telephone:** 07810 131 737.
**OS Grid Ref:** SP 877397.
**Operator:** Willen Miniature Railway Ltd.
**Website:** www.whitecap.co.uk
**Gauge:** 7¼ inch.
**Line Length:** 600 yards, balloon loop.
**First Opened:** 1989.

| No | Name | Type | Builder | Built |
|----|------|------|---------|-------|
|  |  | 4w-4wPH | F Kenny | 2001 |
|  |  | 4w-4wDH | F Kenny | 2005 |

# AREA 4: WEST MIDLANDS

Gloucestershire, Shropshire, Staffordshire, Warwickshire, West Midlands, Worcestershire.

## BAGGERIDGE MINIATURE RAILWAY

Operation at this club track in a public park takes place from Easter until September, generally fortnightly on Sundays and Bank Holidays. Locomotives normally running for the public are "Baggeridge Ranger" and/or "Lady Wulfruna", both with 5 hp hydraulic drives built by Society members. There is also 420 feet of raised 5 inch & 3½ inch gauge track here.

**Address:** Wolverhampton & District MES, Baggeridge Country Park, Gospel End, Dudley, West Midlands, DY3 4HB.
**Telephone:** 01902 753 795.
**OS Grid Ref:** SO 898930.
**Operator:** Wolverhampton & District Model Engineering Society.
**Gauge:** 5 inch/7¼ inch.
**Line Length:** 300 yards, complex.
**First Opened:** 1997.

| No | Name | Type | Builder | Built |
|---|---|---|---|---|
| | Lady Wulfruna | 4wPH | Wulfrun & DMES | 1992 |
| | Baggeridge Ranger | 4w-4wPH | Wolverhampton & DMES | 2005 |

▲ "Nikki Louise" completes the woodland section of track at the Watford Miniature Railway in August 2010.
**Peter Bryant**

▲ "Osprey" pauses at Far Leys Station on the new extension at the Echills Wood Railway at Kingsbury Water Park on 5 June 2011. **Dave Holroyde**

▼ St Egwin, an 0-4-0T+T built by Exmoor Steam Railway, is seen on the Evesham Vale Light Railway on 2 August 2009. **Peter Bryant**

# CATTLE COUNTRY RAILWAY

The railway was opened by Bob Symes of BBC's Tomorrows World in April 2005. Originally built by Joe Nemeth, it was the home of many pieces of equipment from the Oakhill Manor Railway. Joe handed operation over to Cattle Country Park in 2007. The line is an out and back journey of nearly one mile and is worked by a steam outline locomotive specially built for the railway. A recent addition to the line is an extension which terminates at Oakhill station where passengers can alight. This area has been developed with farm trails, picnic areas and pets corner.

**Address:** Cattle Country Adventure Park, Berkeley, Gloucestershire, GL13 9EW.
**Telephone:** 01453 810 510.
**OS Grid Ref:** ST 693993.
**Operator:** Cattle Country Adventure Park.
**Website:** www.cattlecountry.co.uk
**Gauge:** 10¼ inch.
**Line Length:** 500 yards, end to end.
**First Opened:** 2005.

Site Entry Fee

| No | Name | Type | Builder | Built |
|----|------|------|---------|-------|
| | | S/O 0-6-2DH | Cattle Country/J Nemeth | 2008 |

# COALYARD MINIATURE RAILWAY

This line runs from a terminus in front of Kidderminster Railway Museum at the Severn Valley Railway's Kidderminster Town Station. It operates out and back parallel to the Severn Valley Railway platforms. All funds raised go towards improving the miniature railway or are donated to restoration projects on the SVR. The railway operates most weekends from March to December, plus most school holidays. Most operation is by members' locos and there is regular steam operation. Catering facilities are available in the museum and the SVR station. An up-to-date list of operation days can be found by visiting the railway's Facebook page.

**Address:** Severn Valley Railway, Kidderminster Town Station, Comberton Hill, Kidderminster, Worcestershire, DY10 1QX.
**Telephone:** 0121 552 5148 (Evenings).
**OS Grid Ref:** SO 837762.
**Operator:** Coalyard Railway Model Engineering Society.
**Gauge:** 7¼ inch.
**Line Length:** 500 yards, end to end.
**First Opened:** 1988.

| No | Name | Type | Builder | Built |
|----|------|------|---------|-------|
| | Allan A | 0-4-0ST+T | K Wilson | 1999 |
| | | S/O 4wPH | R Dawson | 1992 |

# COLEFORD GWR MUSEUM MINIATURE RAILWAY

A circular line running around this museum in the old goods shed at Coleford. A further four locomotives are on display inside the building. There is also a standard gauge Peckett 0-4-0ST on display here.

**Address:** Coleford GWR Museum, Old Goods Shed, Coleford, Gloucestershire, GL16 8RH.
**Telephone:** 01594 833 569/01594 832 032 (Evenings).
**OS Grid Ref:** SO 577105.
**Operator:** M Rees.
**Website:** www.colefordgwr.150.com
**Gauge:** 7¼ inch.
**Line Length:** 200 yards, circular.
**First Opened:** 1988.

Site entry fee

| No | Name | Type | Builder | Built |
|----|------|------|---------|-------|
| 2091 | Victor | 0-4-0ST | K Hardy | c1984 |
| | Maud | 0-4-0WT | M Rees | U/C |
| | Little John | 4-4wBER | T Smith | 1979 |

# ECHILLS WOOD RAILWAY

A fascinating line from Harvesters station to Far Leys, featuring bridges, tunnels and a huge locomotive depot. A wide variety of steam locomotives operate here at various times and there are monthly special events in the summer months. Harvesters station now has three platforms.

**Address:** Kingsbury Water Park, Bodymoor Heath Road, Kingsbury, Warwickshire, B76 0DY.
**Telephone:** 01926 498 705 (Evenings).
**OS Grid Ref:** SP 205960.
**Operator:** Echills Wood Railway.
**Website:** www.ewr.org.uk
**Gauge:** 7¼ inch.
**Line Length:** 1500 yards, circuit.
**First Opened:** 2006.

| No | Name | Type | Builder | Built |
|---|---|---|---|---|
| | River Avon | 4w-4wDH | G Cox | 1983 |
| DH1 | River Cole | 4w-4wDH | Walters/Bailey | 1989 |

# EVESHAM VALE LIGHT RAILWAY

This line runs through the old orchards and around the 120 acre country park with fine views over the Vale of Evesham. Trains run from Twyford Downs station, which is situated next to the car park, and where there is a station building, engine shed/workshops and a station canopy which doubles as a carriage shed.

**Address:** Evesham Country Park, Twyford, Evesham, Worcestershire, WR11 4TP.
**Telephone:** 01386 422 282.
**OS Grid Ref:** SP 044465.
**Operator:** A & S Corke.  ADRIAN & SANDRA
**Website:** www.evlr.co.uk
**Gauge:** 15 inch.
**Line Length:** 1200 yards, balloon loop.
**First Opened:** 2002.

| No | Name | Type | Builder | Built |
|---|---|---|---|---|
| 32 | Count Louis | 4-4-2 | Bassett Lowke | 1924 |
| | Dougal | 0-6-2T+T | Severn Lamb | 1970 |
| | St Egwin | 0-4-0T+T | Exmoor Steam Railway | 2003 |
| J6F4 | Sludge | 4wDM | Lister | 1955 |
| | Cromwell | 4wDH | Ruston & Hornsby | 1960 |
| | | 4wPMR | M Eddy/M Nowell | 2004 |

# FOXFIELD MINIATURE RAILWAY

This short line is located at Caverswall Road station on this standard gauge former colliery line. The Ride on Railways locomotive here is 5 inch gauge, and it is £1 per ride.

**Address:** Foxfield Railway, Blythe Bridge, Stoke-on-Trent, Staffordshire, ST4 8YT.
**Telephone:** 01782 259 667/01782 396 210.
**OS Grid Ref:** SJ 958421.
**Operator:** Foxfield Miniature Railway.
**Website:** www.foxfieldminiaturerailway.co.uk
**Gauge:** 5 inch/7¼ inch.
**Line Length:** ¾ mile, balloon loop.
**First Opened:** 2008.

Railway entry fee

| No | Name | Type | Builder | Built |
|---|---|---|---|---|
| 21 | Scamp | 4wPH | A Bimpson | 1979 |
| | | 4wBE | P Civil | 2010 |
| D624 | | 0-6-0PM | | |
| | | 4w-4wPE/BE | | |

# HOLLYBUSH MINIATURE RAILWAY

This immaculately laid circuit runs around two small lakes, and features a tunnel and an embankment. There is a steeply graded spur from the station up to the shed area. The railway services an excellent coarse fishing lake where visiting fishermen can purchase day tickets. Journey time is approximately 7 minutes.

**Address:** Hollybush Garden Centre, Warstone Road, Shareshill, Staffordshire, WV10 7LX.
**Telephone:** 01922 418 050.
**OS Grid Ref:** SJ 966064.
**Operator:** B Whalley.
**Website:** www.westonrail.co.uk
**Gauge:** 7¼ inch.
**Line Length:** 950 yards, circuit.
**First Opened:** 1996.

| No | Name | Type | Builder | Built |
|---|---|---|---|---|
| 645 | | 4-4wPH | R Greatrex | 1998 |

▲ 645 is seen at Hollybush Central awaiting passengers on the Hollybush Miniature Railway in July 2010.
**Peter Bryant**

# Denver Light Railway

## Locomotive Engineers

Unit 5 Fryers Close

Bloxwich

Walsall

West Midlands

WS2 2XQ

TEL 01922 404911

Building new locomotives

Restoring old locomotives

Complete overhauls

Track work

Points/crossings

Turntables

Coaching stock

UP to 15 inch gauge

Trailer Canopies

**Contact Andy Walton**
**andrew.walton@denverlightrailway.co.uk**
**www.denverlightrailway.co.uk**

# LEASOWES MINIATURE RAILWAY

The line runs along a canal towpath with views overlooking the lake and park, which is grade one listed.

**Address:** Leasowes Park, Mucklow Hill, Halesowen, Dudley, West Midlands, B62 8DH.
**Telephone:** 01562 710 614 (Evenings).
**OS Grid Ref:** SO 976840.
**Operator:** M Male.
**Gauge:** 7¼ inch.
**Line Length:** 250 yards, end to end.
**First Opened:** 1990.

| No | Name | Type | Builder | Built |
|---|---|---|---|---|
| 46210 | Prince Edward | 2-6-2 | J & W Gower | 1936 |
| 60092 | William Shenstone | 4-4wPM | M Male | 1991 |

# PERRYGROVE RAILWAY & TREETOP ADVENTURE

Situated just to the south of Coleford, Michael Crofts' railway is based firmly on the minimum gauge principles first promoted by Sir Arthur Heywood a hundred years ago. The line takes the form of a squashed "S"; trains double back upon themselves at a higher level, before sweeping round and climbing the grade to Oakiron. Children can follow the clues to be rewarded with discoveries of treasure. "Ursula" is a replica of one of Sir Arthur Heywood's locomotives built for the Eaton Hall Railway; it is based here but may visit other railways occasionally. The railway also houses a collection of original Heywood equipment. The Garratt was imported from Tasmania. Visitors with children can also enjoy the unique Treetop Adventure which has wheelchair and buggy access to five houses up in the trees, an indoor village with secret passages, and a covered picnic and play area near Oakiron station.

**Address:** Perrygrove Farm, Coleford, Gloucestershire, GL16 8QB.
**Telephone:** 01594 834 991.
**OS Grid Ref:** SO 578095.
**Operator:** Treasure Train Ltd.
**Website:** www.perrygrove.co.uk
**Gauge:** 15 inch.
**Line Length:** 1200 yards, end to end.
**First Opened:** 1996.

Site entry fee

| No | Name | Type | Builder | Built |
|---|---|---|---|---|
| | Bush Mill No.3 | 0-4-0+0-4-0T | Bush Mill Railway | 1990 |
| | Spirit of Adventure | 0-6-0T | Exmoor Steam Railway | 1993 |
| | Ursula | 0-6-0T | J Waterfield | 1999 |
| | Lydia | 2-6-2T | Alan Keef | 2008 |
| | | 4wDM | Lister | 1954 |
| 2 | Workhorse | 4wDM | Motor Rail | 1963 |
| | Jubilee | 4wDH | Hunslet | 1994 |

# RUDYARD LAKE STEAM RAILWAY

This line runs along a wooded standard gauge trackbed, from the free car park to The Dam, Lakeside, and Hunthouse Wood; a very attractive setting for a miniature railway. There is a passing loop at Lakeside and two trains often run in summer. As well as the extensive locomotive fleet, there are 12 coaches and 8 wagons on site.

**Address:** Rudyard Old Station, Rudyard, Leek, Staffordshire, ST13 8PF.
**Telephone:** 01995 672 280.
**OS Grid Ref:** SJ 956579. *Stock of Mull Rail acquired 2015*
**Operator:** M Hanson.
**Website:** www.rlsr.org
**Gauge:** 10¼ inch.
**Line Length:** 1½ miles, end to end.
**First Opened:** 1985.

| No | Name | Type | Builder | Built |
|----|------|------|---------|-------|
| 196 | Waverley | 4-4-2 | D Curwen | 1952 |
| | Victoria | 2-6-2T | D Vere | 1993 |
| 6 | Excalibur | 2-4-2T | Exmoor Steam Railway | 1993 |
| 9 | Pendragon | 2-4-2T | Exmoor Steam Railway | 1994 |
| 7 | Merlin | 2-4-2T | Exmoor Steam Railway | 1998 |
| 8 | King Arthur | 0-6-2T | Exmoor Steam Railway | 2005 |
| 2 | Mordred | 4wPM | T Stanhope | c1969 |
| 5 | Rudyard Lady | 4-4wDM | L Smith | 1989 |

## SAFARI EXPRESS

This Severn Lamb train ferries visitors from a station near the park entrance round to the "leisure area" where many other amusement rides can be found. There is also a 40 cm gauge Dotto/ Severn Lamb S/O 4-6-0RE powered line here.

**Address:** West Midland Safari & Leisure Park, Spring Grove, Bewdley, Worcestershire, DY12 1LF.
**Telephone:** 01299 402 114.
**OS Grid Ref:** SO 805756.
**Operator:** West Midlands Safari & Leisure Park.
**Website:** www.wmsp.co.uk
**Gauge:** 15 inch.
**Line Length:** 700 yards, end to end.
**First Opened:** 1979.

Park entry fee

| No | Name | Type | Builder | Built |
|----|------|------|---------|-------|
| | | S/O 2-8-0DH | Severn Lamb | 1979 |

▲ 8 "King Arthur" is the largest of the Exmoor Steam Railway built locomotives at the Rudyard Lake Steam Railway. It is seen here in 2011 at The Dam, halfway up the line. **Peter Bryant**

# TRENTHAM FERN MINIATURE RAILWAY

This line has a small balloon loop at one end and a turntable at the other, and runs through the famous gardens alongside the lake.

**Address:** Trentham Estate, Stone Road, Trentham, Stoke-on-Trent, Staffordshire, ST4 8AX.
**Telephone:** 01782 646 646.
**OS Grid Ref:** SJ 867404.
**Operator:** R Greatrex.
**Website:** www.trentham.co.uk
**Gauge:** 7¼ inch.
**Line Length:** 700 yards, end to end.
**First Opened:** 2005.

Park entry fee

| No | Name | Type | Builder | Built |
|----|------|------|---------|-------|
| | Lady Madcap | 0-4-0ST | K Massey | 1991 |
| 6610 | | 4-4wPH | R Greatrex | 2003 |
| | Trentham Fern | 6wPH | R Greatrex | 2005 |

# WESTON PARK RAILWAY

One of the longest and best maintained 7¼ inch gauge lines. Trains run from the adventure playground at Weston Central, over the bridge across a lake and pass Lakeside station (used occasionally in close season) then they climb back through Weston Central and proceed onto a single line to Temple Wood where they return via a balloon loop to their start point at Weston Central. Journey time is approximately 12 minutes. The railway runs through an outstanding collection of mature trees on the Weston Park Estate. A large shed was built in 2011 which can house a number of visiting steam locomotives, some of which may appear during the operating season.

**Address:** Weston Park, Weston under Lizard, Near Shifnal, Staffordshire, TF11 8LE.
**Telephone:** 01952 852 100.
**OS Grid Ref:** SJ 808106.
**Operator:** B Whalley.
**Website:** www.westonrail.co.uk
**Gauge:** 7¼ inch.
**Line Length:** 1.2 miles, dumb-bell.
**First Opened:** 1980.

Park entry fee

| No | Name | Type | Builder | Built |
|----|------|------|---------|-------|
| | Merlin | 4w-4wDH | B Whalley | 2000 |

# WOODSEAVES MINIATURE RAILWAY

The line runs around the nursery and includes a bridge over a pond and a tunnel constructed from willow. The railway is closed in January, February and November, and runs Sundays from 11.00 to 17.00 the rest of the year. For Saturday openings and event details please see the website or contact the operator for details. Groups and clubs welcome, but please telephone in advance.

**Address:** Woodseaves Garden Plants Nursery, Near Market Drayton, Shropshire, TF9 2AS.
**Telephone:** 01630 653 161.
**OS Grid Ref:** SJ 687305.
**Operator:** W Haywood.
**Website:** www.woodseavesminirail.co.uk
**Gauge:** 7¼ inch.
**Line Length:** 450 yards, complex.
**First Opened:** 2004.

| No | Name | Type | Builder | Built |
|----|------|------|---------|-------|
| | Jean | 0-4-0 | R Bennett | 1994 |
| | Sydney | 0-4-0PH | Roanoke | 2003 |

# AREA 5: EAST MIDLANDS

Derbyshire, Leicestershire, Nottinghamshire.

## HALL LEYS MINIATURE RAILWAY

A simple line running up and down the side of Hall Leys Park.

**Address:** Hall Leys Park, Crown Square, Matlock, Derbyshire, DE4 3AT.
**Telephone:** 07525 217 116.
**OS Grid Ref:** SK 300600.
**Operator:** Miniature Railway Co Ltd.
**Gauge:** 9½ inch.
**Line Length:** 200 yards, end to end.
**First Opened:** 1948.

| No | Name | Type | Builder | Built |
|----|------|------|---------|-------|
| | Little David | 6wDH | Allcock/Coleby Simkins | 1974 |

## IRON MOOSE EXPRESS

This line operates within a children's theme park using stock formerly operated at the American Adventure Theme Park.

**Address:** Twinlakes Family Theme Park, Melton Spinney Road, Melton Mowbray, Leicestershire, LE14 4SB.
**Telephone:** 01664 567 777.
**OS Grid Ref:** SK 771210.
**Operator:** Twinlakes Family Theme Park.
**Website:** www.twinlakespark.co.uk
**Gauge:** 15 inch.
**Line Length:** 1000 yards, balloon loop.
**First Opened:** 2008.

Site Entry Fee

| No | Name | Type | Builder | Built |
|----|------|------|---------|-------|
| 1423 | | S/O 2-6-0DH | Severn Lamb | 1986 |
| | | S/O 2-6-0DH | Severn Lamb | 1988 |

## LEICESTER SOCIETY OF MODEL ENGINEERS

A 2½ inch/3½ inch/5 inch gauge elevated track is located inside the ground level track here.

**Address:** Abbey Park, Leicester, Leicestershire, LE4 5AQ.
**OS Grid Ref:** SK 584055.
**Operator:** Leicester Society of Model Engineers.
**Website:** www.lsme.org.uk
**Gauge:** 5 inch/7¼ inch.
**Line Length:** 750 yards, circular.
**First Opened:** 1988.

| No | Name | Type | Builder | Built |
|----|------|------|---------|-------|
| 5259 | | 2-6-0 | G Smith | 1959 |
| | Romulus | 0-4-0WT+T | Driver/Finnemore | 1989 |
| | Romulus | 0-4-0WT+T | Driver/Finnemore | 1989 |
| | B A Riley | 0-4-0ST | R Gilbert | 1994 |
| 1366 | | 0-6-0PT | S Nipper | 1999 |
| | Buffalo Bill | 2-6-2T | R Burns | 2003 |
| | Meeyes-Mile | 0-4-0T | R Durrant | 2009 |
| 08437 | | 0-6-0BE | D Jeavons/S Nipper | c1997 |
| 519 | | 4-4wPH | J Stubbs | 2000 |
| | | 0-4-0BE | M Banyard | |

# MANOR PARK MINIATURE RAILWAY

The station here has a run-round loop, and the balloon loop can be used as a circuit. There are spurs off the balloon loop to the carriage and loco sheds.

**Address:** Manor Park Road, Glossop, Derbyshire, SK23 0QJ.
**Telephone:** 07779 601 180 (Evenings).
**OS Grid Ref:** SE 041945.
**Operator:** A Sowden.
**Website:** www.highpeak.gov.uk
**Gauge:** 7¼ inch.
**Line Length:** 600 yards, balloon loop.
**First Opened:** 1970.

| No | Name | Type | Builder | Built |
|---|---|---|---|---|
| D7001 | Galahad | 4w-4wBE | Cromar White | 1970 |
| | Manor | 4wPH | Pfeifferbahn/A Sowden | 1993 |
| 1001 | | 4 car BER | A Sowden/J Pinder | 1996 |
| 67005 | | 4-4wBE | S Hurley | 2004 |
| 519 | | 4w-4wBE | A Sowden | 2012 |
| | | 4w-4wBE | A Sowden | 2012 |
| | | 4w-4wDH | A Sowden | U/C |

▲ D5905 "City of Derby" pauses at Mundy Halt with a rake of ex-Fairbourne Railway carriages, on the Markeaton Park Light Railway.
**Michael Rogan**

# MARKEATON PARK LIGHT RAILWAY

This railway has been greatly extended and improved since it was taken over by John and Jane Bull in 1996. Trains now run from the main car park (entrance from the A38 Derby ring road) through the park and over two major bridges to a second terminus adjacent to the play area at Mundy Halt. There are three luxurious enclosed coaches built by Exmoor Steam Railway.

**Address:** Markeaton Park, Derby, Derbyshire, DE22 4AA.
**Telephone:** 01623 552 292 (Evenings).
**OS Grid Ref:** SK 334372.
**Operator:** J & J Bull.
**Gauge:** 15 inch.
**Line Length:** 1400 yards, end to end.
**First Opened:** 1989.

| No | Name | Type | Builder | Built |
|---|---|---|---|---|
| D5905 | City of Derby | 4w-4wDM | J Brown | 1995 |

# MELTON MOWBRAY MINIATURE RAILWAY

A simple line running around the bowling green and play area, next to the River Eye.

**Address:** Leicester Road Sportsground, Leicester Road, Melton Mowbray, Leicestershire, LE13 0DA.
**Telephone:** 07966 583 150 (Evenings).
**OS Grid Ref:** SK 750190.
**Operator:** Melton Mowbray Town Estate.
**Website:** www.meltonmowbraytownestate.co.uk
**Gauge:** 10¼ inch.
**Line Length:** 500 yards, circular.
**First Opened:** 1975.

| No | Name | Type | Builder | Built |
|---|---|---|---|---|
| 1 | | 2w-2PM | G Wilcox | 1968 |

▲ 1 "Smokey Joe" pulls its train of Minirail carriages up the gradient into Loxley station at the Sherwood Forest Railway in September 2008.                    **Peter Bryant**

# NOTTINGHAM SOCIETY OF MODEL ENGINEERS

The track is located within the Nottingham Transport Heritage Centre. Trains run from Little Ruddington station around a loop track of approx 1000 yards, which includes a tunnel; there is also a short branch to a terminal station at Parkgate.

**Address:** Nottingham Transport Heritage Centre, Ruddington, Nottinghamshire, NG11 6NX.
**Telephone:** 0115 940 5705.
**OS Grid Ref:** SK 574322.
**Operator:** Nottingham Society of Model & Experimental Engineers Ltd.
**Website:** www.nsmee.org.uk
**Gauge:** 7¼ inch.
**Line Length:** 1000 yards, circular.
**First Opened:** 1998.

Site entry fee

# PAVILION GARDENS MINIATURE RAILWAY

A circuit through the park, crossing two bridges over a stream. The line was formerly 10¼ inch gauge, and was rebuilt using 12¼ inch gauge track during winter 1999/2000.

**Address:** Pavilion Gardens, St Johns Road, Buxton, Derbyshire, SK17 6BE.
**Telephone:** 01298 23114.
**OS Grid Ref:** SK 055734.
**Operator:** High Peak Borough Council.
**Website:** www.pavilliongardens.co.uk
**Gauge:** 12¼ inch.
**Line Length:** 300 yards, circular.
**First Opened:** 1972.

| No | Name | Type | Builder | Built |
|----|------|------|---------|-------|
| 2000 | Edward Milner | S/O 0-6-0DH | A Keef | 2000 |

# QUEENS PARK MINIATURE RAILWAY

A train of Severn Lamb stock running around the lake in this public park. One trip is two circuits.

**Address:** Queens Park, Boythorpe Road, Chesterfield, Derbyshire, S40 2ND.
**Telephone:** 01246 345 555.
**OS Grid Ref:** SK 379709.
**Operator:** Chesterfield Borough Council.
**Website:** www.chesterfield.gov.uk
**Gauge:** 10¼ inch.
**Line Length:** 550 yards, circular.
**First Opened:** 1976.

| No | Name | Type | Builder | Built |
|----|------|------|---------|-------|
| | Puffin' Billy | S/O 2-6-0DH | Severn Lamb | 1988 |

# SHERWOOD FOREST RAILWAY

The steam and battery locomotives here previously ran on a private railway in Gloucestershire. A steam locomotive is under construction off site. The locomotives are 5/8th scale.

**Address:** Gorsethorpe Road, Edwinstowe, Near Mansfield, Nottinghamshire, NG21 9HL.
**Telephone:** 01623 515 339 (Evenings).
**OS Grid Ref:** SK 586655.
**Operator:** Colley's of Sherwood.
**Website:** www.sherwoodforestrailway.com
**Gauge:** 15 inch.
**Line Length:** 800 yards, end to end (1 mile ride).
**First Opened:** 2000.

| No | Name | Type | Builder | Built |
|----|------|------|---------|-------|
| 1 | Smokey Joe | 0-4-0ST+T | K Hardy | 1991 |
| 2 | Pet | 0-4-0ST+T | K Hardy | 1998 |
| 5 | Pioneer | 2-2wPM | K Rosewell | 1947 |
| BE3 | Anne | 4wBE | K Hardy | 1993 |
| 4 | Lottie | 4wPH | Colley's of Sherwood | 2006 |

# TWYCROSS ZOO MINIATURE RAILWAY

The line here includes a spiral section.

**Address:** Twycross Zoo World Primate Centre, Burton Road, Near Atherstone, Leicestershire, CV9 3PX.
**Telephone:** 0844 474 1777.
**OS Grid Ref:** SK 320061.
**Operator:** East Midland Zoological Society.
**Website:** www.twycrosszoo.org
**Gauge:** 10¼ inch.
**Line Length:** 650 yards, circular.
**First Opened:** 1969.

Zoo entry fee

| No | Name | Type | Builder | Built |
|----|------|------|---------|-------|
| | | S/O 2-8-0DH | Severn Lamb | 1983 |

# WHEELGATE PARK RAILWAY

The railway is located in a children's adventure park and the locomotive here is petrol powered, but features the synchronised sound of a steam locomotive.

**Address:** Wheelgate Adventure Park, White Post Corner, Farnsfield, Nottinghamshire, NG22 8HX.
**Telephone:** 01623 882 773.
**OS Grid Ref:** SK 627572.
**Operator:** Wheelgate Adventure Park.
**Website:** www.wheelgatepark.com
**Gauge:** 7¼ inch.
**Line Length:** 400 yards, balloon loop.
**First Opened:** 1996.

Park entry fee

| No | Name | Type | Builder | Built |
|----|------|------|---------|-------|
| 2 | Mickey | S/O 4w-2PH | R Greatrex | 1999 |

SFR
KEEP
TO
PATH

▲ Another view of 1 "Smokey Joe" at the Sherwood Forest Railway. This picture was taken on 7 April 2012.

John Binch

# AREA 6: EASTERN COUNTIES

Cambridgeshire, Essex, Lincolnshire, Norfolk, Suffolk.

## AUDLEY END MINIATURE RAILWAY

A racetrack of a line with an impressive array of locomotives on shed, from a Great Northern Atlantic to an enormous Denver & Rio Grande 2-8-2. Audley End station has its own car park not far from the entrance drive to the house. After passing the shed area, trains bowl along a long straight, then cross the River Fulfen and River Cam. They then enter a very long and curvaceous balloon loop through the woods, passing Forest Deep Halt, and through a long tunnel. The loop points are centre sprung, so alternate trains take this section in opposite directions before returning from whence they came. Watch out for the teddy bears that live in the woods! There is an outdoor cafe and children's play area on site.

**Address:** Audley End House, Saffron Walden, Essex, CB11 4JB.
**Telephone:** 01799 541 354.
**OS Grid Ref:** TL 523379.
**Operator:** Lord Braybrooke.
**Website:** www.audley-end-railway.co.uk
**Gauge:** 10¼ inch.
**Line Length:** 1 mile, dumb-bell.
**First Opened:** 1964.

| No | Name | Type | Builder | Built |
|----|------|------|---------|-------|
| 3548 | Lord Braybrooke | 2-6-2 | D Curwen | 1948 |
| 4433 | | 4-4-2 | Curwen & Newbery | 1965 |
| 489 | Sara Lucy | 2-8-2 | D Curwen | 1977 |
| 24 | Bruce | 2-6-2 | D Curwen | 1991 |
| | Barbara Curwen | 2-4-2ST+T | D Curwen | 1997 |
| 682 | Doris | 0-6-0PM | D Curwen | 1982 |
| 691 | Henrietta Jane | 0-4-0+0-4-0DH | A Crowhurst | 1991 |

## BARLEYLANDS MINIATURE RAILWAY

This railway opened in 1989 utilising the track and most of the rolling stock from the North Benfleet Miniature Railway. Since then one new locomotive, "Gowrie" has been added. Trains run from the visitor centre to Littlewood Junction. There are five steam locomotives, all of which are currently under overhaul whilst the Roanoke operates trains.

**Address:** Barleylands Visitor Centre, Barleylands Road, Billericay, Essex, CM11 2UD.
**Telephone:** 01268 290 229.
**OS Grid Ref:** TQ 695920.
**Operator:** H R Philpot and Son (Barleylands) Ltd.
**Website:** www.barleylands.co.uk
**Gauge:** 7¼ inch.
**Line Length:** 300 yards, complex.
**First Opened:** 1989.

Park entry fee

| No | Name | Type | Builder | Built |
|----|------|------|---------|-------|
| | Maid of Benfleet | 4-4-2T | J Clarke | 1970 |
| | Vulcan | 2-6-0 | J Clarke | 1972 |
| 92203 | Black Prince | 2-10-0 | J Clarke | 1981 |
| 70000 | Britannia | 4-6-2 | J Clarke | 1981 |
| | (Gowrie) | 0-6-4T | H Dyson | 1990 |
| | Dereck | 0-4-0PH | Roanoke | 2006 |

# BARNARDS MINIATURE RAILWAY

Barnards Farm Gardens cover 17 hectares with landscaped walks, young woodland and a Japanese garden. An engine shed, two stations and a bridge have been built so far. For 2012, the line has been extended up to the "Sittouterie", making the line almost 1¼ miles in length.

**Address:** Barnards Farm, Brentwood Road, West Horndon, Essex, CM13 2LX.
**Telephone:** 01277 811 262.
**OS Grid Ref:** TQ 634877.
**Operator:** Barnards Farm.
**Website:** www.barnardsfarm.eu
**Gauge:** 7¼ inch.
**Line Length:** 1¼ miles, end to end.
**First Opened:** 2010.

| No | Name | Type | Builder | Built |
|----|------|------|---------|-------|
| | Ernie Turner | 0-4-2 | J Forshaw | 1990 |
| | Thomas | 0-6-0T | P & W Moore | c1995 |
| | | 4w-4BER | Mardyke | c1978 |
| D9019 | Royal Highland Fusilier | 6w-6wPH | Mardyke | 1979 |
| D7096 | | 4w-4wDH | Mardyke | c1997 |
| | Blue Pullman | 4w-4PH | Mardyke | 2005 |
| 21 | Marie Dadswell | 4w-4wBE | Compass House | 2009 |

▲ 3548 "Lord Braybrooke", a Curwen 2-6-2, passes through the woods at the Audley End Miniature Railway in 2006. **Audley End Railway**

# BELTON LIGHT RAILWAY

The Belton Light Railway runs through the woodland area of the National Trust property Belton House. Trains are operated by the push and pull method, trains running from the station next to a childrens adventure playground, over a level crossing and through a tunnel to reach the end of the line. Trains then reverse back to the station. There is a footbridge and a two-road engine shed at the station. Originally trains were steam worked and have been operated by various Mardyke locos over the years.

**Address:** Belton House Park & Gardens, Belton, Near Grantham, Lincolnshire, NG32 2LS.
**Telephone:** 01476 566 116.
**OS Grid Ref:** SK 927394.
**Operator:** The National Trust.
**Website:** www.nationaltrust.org.uk/beltonhouse
**Gauge:** 7¼ inch.
**Line Length:** 500 yards, end to end.
**First Opened:** 1979.

Grounds entry fee

| No | Name | Type | Builder | Built |
|----|------|------|---------|-------|
| 4 | Moondial Express | 4w-4wDH | Mardyke | 2005 |
| | | 4w-4wDH | Mardyke | 2011 |

▲ Tank locomotive 8 (to be named during 2012) is seen at the Bure Valley Railway on 28 July 2011. The Bure Valley Railway is a 9 mile line running on the former BR trackbed. **Dave Holroyde**

# BRESSINGHAM STEAM MUSEUM AND GARDENS

These miniature lines form two of the attractions at Bressingham Steam Museum. Trains on the Waveney Valley Railway are timed to coincide with those on the 2 foot gauge Nursery Line, which crosses over it, so that passengers can see the other train at work. The Garden Railway is an enlarged version of a 9½ inch gauge line which dated back to Bressingham's first public opening. A 12 inch gauge 4-4-0T is on display in the museum here.

**Address:** Diss, Norfolk, IP22 2AB.
**Telephone:** 01379 686 900.
**OS Grid Ref:** TM 080805.
**Operator:** Bressingham Steam Preservation Co Ltd.
**Website:** www.bressingham.co.uk
**Gauge:** Waveney Valley Railway 15 inch; Garden Railway 10¼ inch.
**Line Length:** Waveney Valley Railway 1½ miles, circular; Garden Railway 700 yards, balloon loop.
**First Opened:** Waveney Valley Railway 1973; Garden Railway 1995.

Site entry fee.

## 15 inch gauge:

| No | Name | Type | Builder | Built |
|----|------|------|---------|-------|
| 1662 | Rosenkavalier | 4-6-2 | Krupp | 1937 |
| 1663 | Mannertreu | 4-6-2 | Krupp | 1937 |
| | St Christopher | 2-6-2T | Exmoor Steam Railway | 2001 |
| D6353 | | 4w-4wDM | J Brown | 1998 |

## 10¼ inch gauge:

| No | Name | Type | Builder | Built |
|----|------|------|---------|-------|
| 1 | Alan Bloom | 0-4-0ST | P Gray | 1995 |

# BURE VALLEY RAILWAY

Trains run from Aylsham through Brampton, Buxton and Coltishall to Wroxham; most of the formation is on a standard gauge trackbed. The "ZB" class locos (6, 7, 8 & 9) are among the largest and most powerful 15 inch gauge locomotives ever built. The components have been adapted to tank engine form to create Numbers 8 and 9. No 8 is based on a Vale of Rheidol prototype, whilst no 9 is based on a locomotive from the erstwhile Leek & Manifold Railway. The railway holds many special events including the ever popular Santa trains; the railway also offers driver experience courses. "Greenbat" is currently unpowered and is to be rebuilt.

**Address:** Aylsham, Norfolk, NR11 6BW & Wroxham, Norfolk, NR12 8UU.
**Telephone:** 01263 733 858.
**OS Grid Ref:** TG 303187 (Aylsham).
**Operator:** Bure Valley Railway (1991) Ltd.
**Website:** www.bvrw.co.uk ; Facebook: http://www.facebook.com/BureValleyRailway ;
Twitter: http://twitter.com/BureValley
**Gauge:** 15 inch.
**Line Length:** 8¾ miles, end to end.
**First Opened:** 1990.

| No | Name | Type | Builder | Built |
|----|------|------|---------|-------|
| 1 | Wroxham Broad | 2-6-4T | G&SLE/Winson | 1964 |
| 6 | Blickling Hall | 2-6-2 | Winson Eng | 1994 |
| 7 | Spitfire | 2-6-2 | Winson Eng | 1994 |
| 8 | | 2-6-2T | BVR/Winson | 1997 |
| 9 | Mark Timothy | 2-6-4T | Winson Eng/Alan Keef | 1999 |
| (5) | (Toby) | S/O 4wDM | Lister Blackstone | 1960 |
| 4 | (Rusty) | 4wDH | Hunslet | 1954 |
| | Greenbat | 2-2w-4BE | Greenwood & Batley | 1966 |
| (3) | 2nd Air Division USAAF | 4w-4wDH | J Edwards | 1989 |

# CANVEY RAILWAY & MODEL ENGINEERING CLUB

Open Sundays only - April to October. There is an elevated track adjacent to the ground level one which features a bridge over a stream and a crossing on the level.

**Address:** Waterside Farm Sports Complex, Somnes Avenue, Waterside Farm, Canvey Island, Essex, SS8 9RA.
**OS Grid Ref:** TQ 781849.
**Operator:** Canvey Railway & Model Engineering Club.
**Website:** www.cramec.org
**Gauge:** 7¼ inch.
**Line Length:** 1000 yards, complex.
**First Opened:** 1996.

# CHELMSFORD SOCIETY OF MODEL ENGINEERS

There are 3½ inch, 5 inch and 7¼ inch elevated circuits and 5 inch/7¼ inch ground level circuits here.

**Address:** Meteor Way, Waterhouse Lane, Chelmsford, Essex, CM1 2RL.
**OS Grid Ref:** TL 699066.
**Operator:** Chelmsford Society of Model Engineers.
**Website:** www.csme.50webs.com
**Gauge:** 5 inch /7¼ inch.
**Line Length:** 350 yards, circular.
**First Opened:** 1992.

▲ Two steam locomotives separated by over 75 years! On the right, 1 "Sutton Belle", was built in 1933 and first saw service on the Hardwick Manor Railway. It is seen next to LNER Class O4 6284 of 2009 vintage, at the Cleethorpes Coast Light Railway on 13 August 2011.  **Dave Holroyde**

# CLEETHORPES COAST LIGHT RAILWAY

This is the latest of six different miniature railways to have operated in Cleethorpes over the years, having been regauged from 14½ inch gauge. Trains run from Lakeside Station up the hill past the shed area, then alongside the sea wall to Kingsway. For many years two Severn Lamb "Rio"s were the sole motive power, but the railway now has a good volunteer support group and trains are regularly steam hauled. The line was realigned with a new 40 yard viaduct at the Kingsway end in early 2000, and extended to North Sea Lane in 2007. Also in store here is 18 inch gauge Atlantic "Crompton", built by David Curwen in 1951.

**Address:** Lakeside Station, Kings Road, Cleethorpes, Lincolnshire, DN35 0AG.
**Telephone:** 01472 604 657.
**OS Grid Ref:** TA 315078.
**Operator:** Cleethorpes Coast Light Railway Ltd.
**Website:** www.cleethorpescoastlightrailway.co.uk
**Gauge:** 15 inch.
**Line Length:** 1¼ miles, end to end.
**First Opened:** 1971.

| No | Name | Type | Builder | Built |
|---|---|---|---|---|
| | Mighty Atom | 4-4-2 | Bassett Lowke | 1908 |
| 1 | Sutton Belle | 4-4-2 | Cannon Ironfoundries | 1933 |
| 2 | Sutton Flyer | 4-4-2 | Cannon/Hunt | 1950 |
| | Mountaineer | 0-4-0 | W Van der Heiden | 1970 |
| 111 | Yvette | 4-4-0 | E Craven/T Tate | 1970 |
| 24 | Sandy River | 2-6-2 | Fairbourne | 1990 |
| | Effie | 0-4-0WT | Great Northern Steam | 1999 |
| 6284 | | 2-8-0 | T Turner/R Loxley/R Crome | 2009 |
| No.5 | Battison | S/O 2-6-4DE | S Battison | 1958 |
| 7 | | 4wDM | Lister | 1944 |
| No.4 | | 4-4wPH | G&SLE | 1946 |
| | | 4wPM | Lister | 1950 |
| 3 | The Cub | 4-4wDH | Minirail | 1954 |
| (KD1) | | 4-car DER | Rapido Rail Systems | 1983 |
| DA1 | | 4wDM | Bush Mills Railway | 1986 |

# COLNE VALLEY MINIATURE RAILWAY

The line operates alongside the standard gauge Colne Valley Railway. There is a canopied station. Visiting steam locomotives operate occasionally, include a Romulus and Hercules.

**Address:** Colne Valley Railway, Castle Hedingham, Essex, CO9 3DZ.
**Telephone:** 01787 461 174.
**OS Grid Ref:** TL 773362.
**Operator:** E Bailey.
**Website:** www.cvmrailway.com
**Gauge:** 7¼ inch.
**Line Length:** 350 yards, balloon loop.
**First Opened:** 2008.

Railway entry fee.

| No | Name | Type | Builder | Built |
|---|---|---|---|---|
| | Tom | S/O 4wPH | R Kay | 1983 |
| 2 | | 0-6-0PH | P Willis/J Bailiss | 2005 |
| | Saffron | 4wBE | Compass House | 2006 |
| | Hedingham House | 4w-4wBE | E Bailey | 2009 |

# FERRY MEADOWS MINIATURE RAILWAY

A popular line located in a large public park, a short walk from Ferry Meadows station on the Nene Valley Railway. The track descends from Ham Lane to Gunwade Lane; the loco is turned and runs round its train at each end.

**Address:** Nene Park, Oundle Road, Peterborough, Cambridgeshire, PE2 5UU.
**Telephone:** 01733 234 443.
**OS Grid Ref:** TL 148975.
**Operator:** D & S Coging.
**Website:** www.ferrymeadowsrailway.co.uk
**Gauge:** 10¼ inch.
**Line Length:** 700 yards, end to end.
**First Opened:** 1979.

| No | Name | Type | Builder | Built |
|----|------|------|---------|-------|
| 1 | | S/O 2-8-0PH | Severn Lamb | 1971 |
| | Charles | S/O 0-6-0DH | Alan Keef | 1999 |

# GRIMSBY AND CLEETHORPES MODEL ENGINEERING SOCIETY

A pleasant track which is home to a considerable number of locomotives. Be sure to climb to the top of the adjacent windmill while you are there. No locomotives are kept on site.

**Address:** Waltham Windmill, Brigsley Road, Waltham, Near Grimsby, Lincolnshire, DN37 0JZ.
**OS Grid Ref:** TA 259034.
**Operator:** Grimsby & Cleethorpes Model Engineering Society.
**Website:** www.gcmes.org.uk
**Gauge:** 5 inch/7¼ inch.
**Line Length:** 400 yards, circular.
**First Opened:** 1990.

| No | Name | Type | Builder | Built |
|----|------|------|---------|-------|
| | | 0-4-2T | G Dobbs | c1978 |
| 11 | | 0-6-0T | R Copley | 1988 |
| 1366 | | 0-6-0PT | D Smith | 1990 |
| 32670 | | 0-6-0T | J Britton | 1994 |
| | | 0-4-0ST | B Thompson | 1997 |
| 84008 | | 2-6-2T | J Britton | 1998 |
| | Trevor | 0-4-0ST | T Monk | 1998 |
| 1 | Valerie Anne | 0-4-0ST | Clark/Monk | 1999 |
| 2003 | Earl Marischal | 2-8-2 | D Smith | 2006 |
| 35 | Holmside No.1 | 0-6-0ST | P Gilbey | 2008 |
| 20 | | 0-10-0T | D Smith | 2010 |
| 45157 | The Glasgow Highlander | 4-6-0 | M Halliday | U/C |
| | | 0-4-0PH | Askwith/Monk | 1999 |
| | | 0-6-0BE | Compass House | 1999 |
| 4368 | | 0-4-0PE/BE | M Askwith | 2011 |
| | | 0-6-0BE | | |

# KINGS LYNN & DISTRICT SOME

A small multi-gauge circuit and loop line within the grounds of the leisure centre. Open every Sunday between April and the end of October, 12.00 to 17.00.

**Address:** Lynnsport Leisure Centre, Greenpark Avenue, Kings Lynn, Norfolk, PE30 2NB.
**Telephone:** 01366 381 182 (Evenings).
**OS Grid Ref:** TF 631211.
**Operator:** Kings Lynn & District Society of Model Engineers.
**Website:** www.kldsme.org.uk
**Gauge:** 3½ inch/5 inch/7¼ inch.
**Line Length:** 200 yards, circular.
**First Opened:** 1992.

| No | Name | Type | Builder | Built |
|----|------|------|---------|-------|
| 2 | Romulus | 0-6-0WT | T Cox | c2009 |
| | Bridget | 0-4-2T | | |
| | Alex | 0-6-0T | | |
| | | 6wBE | T Cox | c2005 |
| 4 | | 6wBE | M Coote | 2005 |
| 803 | Mount Lavinia | 4w-4wBE | M Coote | 2007 |
| | Harlech Castle | 0-6-0BE | M Coote/B Cannell | 2009 |
| | Criccieth Castle | 0-6-0BE | M Coote/B Cannell | 2009 |

# LANGFORD AND BEELEIGH RAILWAY

The line is located in the seven acre grounds of the steam pumping station, adjacent to the River Blackwater. Running dates can be found on the Museum of Power website.

**Address:** Museum of Power, Hatfield Road, Langford, Near Maldon, Essex, CM9 6QA.
**Telephone:** 01621 843 183.
**OS Grid Ref:** TL 836090.
**Operator:** Museum of Power.
**Website:** www.museumofpower.org.uk
**Gauge:** 7¼ inch.
**Line Length:** 440 yards, circular.
**First Opened:** 2003.

| No | Name | Type | Builder | Built |
|----|------|------|---------|-------|
| | Hercules | 0-4-0 | L&BR | 2005 |
| | Don | 2-4-2 | L&BR | 2006 |
| | Taw | 2-6-2 | L&BR | 2009 |
| | Blaze | 0-4-0PH | M Chapman | |

▲ On 19 May 2012, 2-4-2ST+T steam locomotive "Barbara Curwen", the final build of locomotive builder David Curwen, passes the Enchanted Fairy Woodland Walk hauling six carriages and a full load of passengers on the Audley End Railway.
**John Binch**

▲ 7 "Spitfire" receives minor attention at Aylsham on the Bure Valley Railway on 28 July 2008.
**Simon Metcalf**

▼ "Densil" waits for fares to be collected at Wells Harbour station before departing for Pinewood on the Wells Harbour Railway on 26 July 2011.　　**Dave Holroyde**

# MABLETHORPE MINIATURE RAILWAY

Before the 1939–45 war, Louis Shaw and Percy Harding Kiff operated some notable public 7¼ inch gauge railways in Mablethorpe. Alas all one can see today is this simple circle of track in a public park behind the sea wall, running through the tunnel/shed as it goes.

**Address:** Queens Park, Mablethorpe, Lincolnshire, LN12 2AS.
**Telephone:** 01507 473 320.
**OS Grid Ref:** TF 510847.
**Operator:** A Smith.
**Gauge:** 7¼ inch.
**Line Length:** 200 yards, circular.
**First Opened:** 1968.

| No | Name | Type | Builder | Built |
|----|------|------|---------|-------|
| | Lewis | S/O 4w-4PM | G Mawby | 1972 |
| | Chitty Chitty Bang Bang | 4-4wPM | G Mawby | 1976 |

# MINI RAIL

A short line forming an attraction additional to the standard gauge exhibits at the East Anglian Railway Museum.

**Address:** East Anglian Railway Museum, Chappel & Wakes Colne Station, Near Colchester, Essex, CO6 2DS.
**Telephone:** 01206 242 524.
**OS Grid Ref:** TL 898289.
**Operator:** East Anglian Railway Museum.
**Website:** www.earm.co.uk
**Gauge:** 5 inch/7¼ inch.
**Line Length:** 200 yards, end to end.
**First Opened:** 1991.

Site entry fee.

| No | Name | Type | Builder | Built |
|----|------|------|---------|-------|
| | Little John | 0-4-0T+T | J Chapman | 1994 |
| | Romulus | 0-4-0WT | Chapman/Martin | 1997 |
| | Charlie | 0-4-0T | Farmer/Chapman/Martin | 2001 |
| | | 0-4-2T | Moors Valley | 2011 |
| | | 4wPM | J Chapman | 1995 |

# NORWICH & DISTRICT SOME

The elevated track in the public park dates from 1960 and the ground level track opened in 2006.

**Address:** Eaton Park, South Park Avenue, Norwich, Norfolk, NR4 7AX.
**Telephone:** 01603 743 372 (Evenings).
**OS Grid Ref:** TG 208075.
**Operator:** Norwich & District Society of Model Engineers.
**Website:** www.friendsofeatonpark.co.uk/railway.html
**Gauge:** 5 inch/7¼ inch.
**Line Length:** 900 yards, circular.
**First Opened:** 2006.

| No | Name | Type | Builder | Built |
|-------|-------------|---------|-------------------------|-------|
| 5042 | | 4-6-0 | Townsend/Dabson/Chester | 1988 |
| 222 | | 0-6-0T | B Baker | 1992 |
| | | 2-6-0 | J Ward | 1993 |
| 4475 | Flying Fox | 4-6-2 | B Baker/Modelworks | 2010 |
| 92220 | Evening Star | 2-10-0 | | |
| 1366 | | 0-6-0PT | | |
| | | 4-6-2 | | |
| | Nelson | 4w-4wBE | | |
| | | 4w-4wBE | | |

# PETTITTS ANIMAL ADVENTURE PARK RAILWAY

Originally 7¼ inch gauge, the line forms one of the attractions in this animal park. Trains run clockwise from Pettitts Junction.

**Address:** Churen Road, Reedham, Norfolk, NR13 3UA.
**Telephone:** 01493 700 094.
**OS Grid Ref:** TG 425025.
**Operator:** Pettitts.
**Website:** www.pettittsadventurepark.co.uk
**Gauge:** 10¼ inch.
**Line Length:** 500 yards, circular.
**First Opened:** 1989.

Park entry fee.

| No | Name | Type | Builder | Built |
|----|------|------|---------|-------|
|    |      | S/O 4w-4wDH | Pettitts | 1990 |

# PLEASUREWOOD HILLS MINIATURE RAILWAY

This line runs from Pleasurewood Hills station through the park, passing through a tunnel into a natural woodland area. There is also a 2 foot gauge circuit which crosses the 7¼ inch gauge, once over a bridge and again on the level. It is unusual to find 7¼ inch gauge working in such a commercial environment.

**Address:** Pleasurewood Hills Family Theme Park, Corton, Lowestoft, Suffolk, NR32 5DZ.
**Telephone:** 01502 586 000.
**OS Grid Ref:** TM 543966.
**Operator:** Pleasurewood Hills Ltd.
**Website:** www.pleasurewoodhills.com; Facebook: www.facebook.com/Pleasurewoodhills
**Gauge:** 7¼ inch.
**Line Length:** 1200 yards, circular.
**First Opened:** 1982.

Park entry fee

| No | Name | Type | Builder | Built |
|----|------|------|---------|-------|
|    | Serendipity | 6w-6wDH | J Edwards | 1981 |
| 19761-0 |  | 6w-6wDH | Edwards/Hudson | 1984 |

# POSTLAND MINIATURE RAILWAY

This line is a balloon loop in a garden centre.

**Address:** Crowland Garden Centre, Postland Road, Crowland, Lincolnshire, PE6 0JB.
**Telephone:** 07984 249 395 (Evenings).
**OS Grid Ref:** TF 249109.
**Operator:** D Oswald.
**Website:** www.thegardencentregroup.co.uk
**Gauge:** 7¼ inch.
**Line Length:** 450 yards, balloon loop.
**First Opened:** 2008.

| No | Name | Type | Builder | Built |
|----|------|------|---------|-------|
| 50031 | Hood | 6w-6PH | D Oswald | 2000 |
| 2051 | Brighton Belle | 4w-4wPE/BE | J Pinder | 2010 |

# SAFFRON WALDEN & DISTRICT SOCIETY OF MODEL ENGINEERS

There is a 3½ inch/5 inch/7¼ inch gauge elevated track here as well as the ground level one. Located adjacent to the Audley End Miniature Railway.

**Address:** Audley End, Saffron Walden, Essex, CB11 4JB.
**OS Grid Ref:** TL 523379.
**Operator:** Saffron Walden & District Society of Model Engineers.
**Website:** www.swdsme.org.uk
**Gauge:** 5 inch/7¼ inch.
**Line Length:** 500 yards, circuit.
**First Opened:** 1989.

# WAT TYLER MINIATURE RAILWAY

A line running through this extensive country park, from the boat museum to the marina. A ½ mile extension was completed in Spring 2011.

**Address:** Wat Tyler Country Park, Pitsea, Essex, SS16 4UH.
**Telephone:** 01268 275 050.
**OS Grid Ref:** TQ 738865.
**Operator:** Go Bonkers Ltd.
**Website:** www.wattylerminiaturerailway.com
**Gauge:** 10¼ inch.
**Line Length:** 1 mile, balloon loop.
**First Opened:** 1988.

| No | Name | Type | Builder | Built |
|----|------|------|---------|-------|
| D7022 | Sid Tyndall | 4w-4PH | Cromar White | 1971 |
| 31327 | | 4w-4PM | Ford | |

▲ The Wells & Walsingham Railway is the longest 10¼ inch gauge line in the world, running two Garratts, the most recent of which is "Norfolk Heroine", just three months old when seen here on 26 July 2011.

**Dave Holroyde**

# WELLS HARBOUR RAILWAY

The line runs from Harbour station at Wells, alongside the Beach Road to Pinewoods, forming a useful transport service to and from a caravan site. The little locomotives must by now have notched up a remarkable mileage. A neat little railway which also has a rake of roofed coaches.

**Address:** Beach Road, Wells next the Sea, Norfolk, NR23 1DR.
**Telephone:** 07939 149 264.
**OS Grid Ref:** TF 915439.
**Operator:** G & A Brecknell.
**Website:** www.wellsharbourrailway.co.uk
**Gauge:** 10¼ inch.
**Line Length:** 1200 yards, end to end.
**First Opened:** 1976.

| No | Name | Type | Builder | Built |
|----|------|------|---------|-------|
| | Densil | S/O 0-6-0DH | Alan Keef | 1998 |
| | Howard | S/O 0-6-0DH | Alan Keef | 2005 |
| | (Weasel) | 4wDH | D King | 1980 |

# WELLS & WALSINGHAM LIGHT RAILWAY

This is the longest 10¼ inch gauge railway in the world, and was also the first 10¼ inch gauge railway to obtain a Light Railway Order. Trains run from the station above Wells next the Sea to Walsingham, along a standard gauge trackbed. The Garretts "Norfolk Hero" and "Norfolk Heroine" take the great majority of services, which run daily from Good Friday to the end of September; the railway has an active volunteer support group. Over the winter of 1998/99 major excavations took place which have removed the worst gradients facing Walsingham bound trains. Visiting private steam locomotives can sometimes be operated here.

**Address:** Wells next the Sea, Norfolk, NR23 1QB.
**Telephone:** 01328 711 630.
**OS Grid Ref:** TF 925430.
**Operator:** R & M Francis.
**Website:** www.wellsandwalsinghamrailway.co.uk
**Gauge:** 10¼ inch.
**Line Length:** 4 miles, end to end.
**First Opened:** 1982.

| No | Name | Type | Builder | Built |
|----|------|------|---------|-------|
| 3 | Norfolk Hero | 2-6-0+0-6-2 | N Simkins | 1986 |
| 6 | Norfolk Heroine | 2-6-0+0-6-2 | Coleby/Mayes/Rowland/TMA | 2011 |
| 2 | Weasel | S/O 6wDH | Alan Keef | 1985 |
| | Norfolk Harvester | 4w-4wDH | A Mills | 1993 |

# AREA 7: NORTH WEST

Cheshire, Cumbria, Greater Manchester, Lancashire, Merseyside.

## ALL-IN-ONE MINIATURE RAILWAY

The circuit runs through the garden centre and growing area. The line features a tunnel and award winning station. Also here is 10, a person powered 2w-2 loco, built by S Parks/D Moss in 2011.

**Address:** All in One Garden Centre, London Road, Allostock, Knutsford, Cheshire, WA16 9LU.
**Telephone:** 01565 722 567.
**OS Grid Ref:** SJ 745711.
**Operator:** D Moss.
**Website:** www.allinone.co.uk
**Gauge:** 7¼ inch.
**Line Length:** 600 yards, circular.
**First Opened:** 2000.

| No | Name | Type | Builder | Built |
|---|---|---|---|---|
| 7 | | S/O 4wBER | Parkside | 1996 |
| 9 | (Biff) | S/O 4wBE | D Moss/A Higgins | 2009 |
| 253007 | HMS Pembroke | 4w-4wBE | Mardyke | 1983 |
| (501) | | 4w-4wBER | Pfeifferbahn | 1989 |
| 812 | | 6w-6wPE | D Smallwood | 1991 |
| 5624/5623 | | 4w-4w+4-4BE | Express Locomotives | 2000 |
| 20035 | | 4w-4wBE | MEP/P Whittaker | 2009 |

▲ Battery electric locomotive 5624/5623, built by Express Locomotives, is seen at the award-winning station at the All-in-One Miniature Railway in Knutsford, Cheshire, on 23 May 2010.  **Dave Holroyde**

# BLACKPOOL ZOO MINIATURE RAILWAY

A line running within the grounds of the zoo from the newly constructed children's farm. During the 2010 winter season, the track route was extensively altered, with a new station and turntable.

**Address:** Blackpool Zoo Park, East Park Drive, Blackpool, Lancashire, FY3 8PP.
**Telephone:** 01253 830 830.
**OS Grid Ref:** SD 335361.
**Operator:** Playbarn.
**Website:** www.blackpoolzoo.org.uk
**Gauge:** 15 inch.
**Line Length:** 700 yards, end to end.
**First Opened:** 1972.

Zoo Entry Fee

| No | Name | Type | Builder | Built |
|----|------|------|---------|-------|
| | | S/O 2-8-0DH | Severn Lamb | 1972 |

# BROOKSIDE MINIATURE RAILWAY

This line runs through a busy garden centre; the scenic route includes five bridges and a 65 foot tunnel. At the station is a replica GWR waiting room, inside which an extensive collection of railwayana is displayed. The steam outline 4wBER locomotives run on their own tracks; put a coin in the slot and drive your own train.

**Address:** Brookside Garden Centre, Macclesfield Road, Poynton, Cheshire, SK12 1BY.
**Telephone:** 01625 872 919.
**OS Grid Ref:** SJ 927852.
**Operator:** C Halsall.
**Website:** www.brooksideminiaturerailway.co.uk
**Gauge:** 7¼ inch.
**Line Length:** 950 yards, circular.
**First Opened:** 1990.

| No | Name | Type | Builder | Built |
|----|------|------|---------|-------|
| | Jane | 0-4-2T | Exmoor Steam Railway | 2000 |
| | Billy May | 2-4-2T | Exmoor Steam Railway | 2000 |
| | Jean | 0-4-2T | Exmoor Steam Railway | 2000 |
| | Amy Louise | 0-4-2T | Exmoor Steam Railway | 2003 |
| | Jeremy | 0-4-2T | Exmoor Steam Railway | 2011 |
| 7 | | S/O 4wBER | Parkside | 1998 |
| 7 | | S/O 4wBER | J Horsfield | 1999 |
| 2000 | Mighty Max | 4w-4wPH | R Greatrex | 2000 |
| 6602 | Sir Richard | 4-4wDH | R Greatrex | 2002 |
| 6610 | Miss Katie | 4w-4wDH | R Greatrex | 2010 |

# BURNLEY & PENDLE MINIATURE RAILWAY SOCIETY

The line is located in a public park and runs partly through a wooded area. The main feature is a 100 foot long bridge.

**Address:** Thompson Park, Burnley, Lancashire, BB11 2AA.
**OS Grid Ref:** SD 844333.
**Operator:** Burnley & Pendle Miniature Railway Society.
**Website:** www.bpmrs.org.uk
**Gauge:** 7¼ inch.
**Line Length:** 900 yards, circuit.
**First Opened:** 2002.

| No | Name | Type | Builder | Built |
|----|------|------|---------|-------|
| | Sarah | 0-4-0+T | G Oughton | 1991 |
| 8390 | Babs | 0-8-0 | J Milsburn | 1998 |
| 2 | J B Earle | 2-6-4T | D Edisbury | 2000 |

| | | | | |
|---|---|---|---|---|
| 1465 | | 0-4-2T | A Middleton | 2008 |
| 68083 | | S/O 4wBE | | |
| 150 001 | | 4 car BER | Parkside | 1990 |
| 6659 | | 4-4wPH | R Greatrex | 1995 |
| 4972 | Furka-Oberalp | 4wBE | P Moon | 1997 |
| | Ruby | 4wBE | D Kitson | 2002 |
| | | 4w-4-4wBER | P Moon/B&P MES | 2008 |
| | Planet | 4wPH | | |

## CARLISLE & DISTRICT MODEL ENGINEERING SOCIETY

An elevated circuit in a public park.

**Address:** Hammonds Pond, Buchanan Road, Upperby, Carlisle, Cumbria, CA2 4SD.
**OS Grid Ref:** NY 405535.
**Operator:** Carlisle & District Model Engineering Society.
**Website:** www.carlisledmes.co.uk
**Gauge:** 5 inch/7¼ inch.
**Line Length:** 200 yards, circular.
**First Opened:** 1947.

# CREWE HERITAGE CENTRE MINIATURE RAILWAY

An unusual line squeezed into the confines of this museum site. Trains leave Crewe (Old Works) terminus, cross over the entrance drive and through a short tunnel to Forge End, where the loco turns and runs round. There is then a straight run between the site perimeter and the prototype Advanced Passenger Train, displayed here, to Midge Bridge, adjacent to Crewe North signal box, where the loco again turns and runs round, before repeating the journey in the opposite direction. A ride on the miniature railway is free, included in the site entry fee.

**Address:** Crewe Heritage Centre, Vernon Way, Crewe, Cheshire, CW1 2DB.
**Telephone:** 01270 212 130.
**OS Grid Ref:** SJ 709553.
**Operator:** Crewe Heritage Centre Miniature Railway Volunteer Group.
**Website:** www.creweheritagecentre.co.uk
**Gauge:** 7¼ inch.
**Line Length:** 600 yards, complex.
**First Opened:** 1992.

Site entry fee.

| No | Name | Type | Builder | Built |
|----|------|------|---------|-------|
| | | 0-6-0T | R Elmore | c1987 |
| | Jenny | 2-4-0ST+T | R Marsh/B Rogers | 1992 |
| | Vulcan | 4w-4BE | Severn Lamb | 1987 |
| D7030 | Norcliff | 4w-4PH | ESSE | 1993 |
| D6327 | Peter White | 4wPH | A Kettle/D Jeavons | 2008 |

▲ 2011, built by LA Services, is seen hauling a full train on the Safari Railway in 2011.  **David Gill**

# DRAGON MINIATURE RAILWAY

Opened as a balloon loop in 1999, this line was extended into a dumb-bell. Trains run from Otterspool Junction; nearby are a turntable and a three-road shed.

**Address:** Marple Garden Centre, Otterspool, Dooley Lane, Marple, Stockport, Greater Manchester, SK6 7HE.
**OS Grid Ref:** SJ 937894.
**Operator:** B Lomas.
**Website:** www.freewebs.com/dragonrailway
**Gauge:** 7¼ inch.
**Line Length:** 500 yards, dumb-bell.
**First Opened:** 1999.

| No | Name | Type | Builder | Built |
|---|---|---|---|---|
| 2 | Marcus | 0-4-0ST+T | A Kay | 1978 |
| 4 | Goliath | 0-4-0T+T | R Kay | 1979 |
| 3 | Lady Pauline | 0-4-2T | R Kay | 1982 |
| | Princess | 0-4-2T | A Edgerton/J Horsfield | 1989 |
| | Danny | 2-4-2 | D & G Sims | 1992 |
| | Jack | 0-4-0WT+T | P Frank | 2002 |
| | Dragonfly | 2-4-0T | P Frank | 2004 |
| D5903 | Andrew | 4w-4PH | B Lomas | 1985 |
| 1 | Tara the Tram | 4wBER | R Kay | c1990 |
| 2 | David | 4-4wPH | N Pendlebury | 1991 |
| D1015 | Western Champion | 6-6wPH | B Lomas | 1993 |
| 47338 | Flying Dragon | 6-6wPH | B Lomas | 1997 |
| D8608 | | 6-6wPH | B Lomas | 2010 |

▲ One of the railway's workhorses waits for passengers on the Windmill Animal Farm Railway on 19th September 2011.
**Jonathan James**

# GULLIVERS RAILROAD

Trains run from the main entrance plaza calling en route at Dinosaurland. There is a bridge over a stream, a footbridge, and several level crossings.

**Address:** Gullivers Warrington, Shackleton Close, Old Hall, Warrington, Cheshire, WA5 5YZ.
**Telephone:** 01925 444 888.
**OS Grid Ref:** SJ 589900.
**Operator:** D Phillips.
**Website:** www.gulliversfun.co.uk
**Gauge:** 15 inch.
**Line Length:** 500 yards, circular.
**First Opened:** 1989.

Park entry fee

| No | Name | Type | Builder | Built |
|----|------|------|---------|-------|
| | | S/O 6+6wDE | Meridian Motioneering | 1989 |

# GROSVENOR PARK MINIATURE RAILWAY

Opened to commemorate the centenary of the Duke of Westminster's railway at nearby Eaton Hall. The line runs over a bridge and circles a duck pond.

**Address:** Grosvenor Park, Grosvenor Park Road, Chester, Cheshire, CH1 1QQ.
**Telephone:** 07530 397 079.
**OS Grid Ref:** SJ 412663.
**Operator:** Grosvenor Park Miniature Railway Ltd.
**Website:** www.gpmr.co.uk
**Gauge:** 7¼ inch.
**Line Length:** 440 yards, circular.
**First Opened:** 1996.

| No | Name | Type | Builder | Built |
|----|------|------|---------|-------|
| | Brenda Isabella | 0-4-0 | | 1996 |
| | Stevie B | 0-4-2T+T | J Horsfield | 2004 |
| 1 | Robin Butterell | 6-6wPH | B Lomas | 2001 |
| 6602 | | 4-4wPH | R Greatrex | 2004 |

# HAIGH RAILWAY

This line runs through woodland in the Country Park surrounding Haigh Hall, with stations at Haigh South and Haigh North. Its original stock came from Fairbourne when that railway changed its gauge. Later they also purchased a steam outline loco and coaches, from Alan Keef Ltd.

**Address:** Haigh Country Park, Haigh, Wigan, Greater Manchester, WN2 1PE.
**Telephone:** 01942 832 895.
**OS Grid Ref:** SD 600083.
**Operator:** Wigan Leisure & Culture Trust.
**Website:** www.wlct.org/haigh
**Gauge:** 15 inch.
**Line Length:** 1 mile, circular.
**First Opened:** 1986.

| No | Name | Type | Builder | Built |
|----|------|------|---------|-------|
| | Helen | S/O 0-6-2DH | Alan Keef | 1992 |
| | Rachel | 0-6-0DM | G&SLE | 1961 |

# HALTON MINIATURE RAILWAY

Trains depart from Mousetrap Hall station, near the ski slope, and shortly bear left onto a very long balloon loop. Halfway along this loop is a chord for trains only taking a "short" journey. There are several passing loops on the way round, some doubling as sidings for works trains or where locos may pause if need be. Quite an extensive line; open days are held during which visiting locomotives may operate. There is now a railway themed children's play area next to the station.

**Address:** Town Park, Palace Fields, Runcorn, Halton, Cheshire, WA7 6PT.
**Telephone:** 01928 701 965.
**OS Grid Ref:** SJ 548811.
**Operator:** Halton Miniature Railway Society Ltd.
**Website:** www.haltonminirail.weebly.com
**Gauge:** 7¼ inch.
**Line Length:** 1 mile, dumb-bell.
**First Opened:** 1980.

| No | Name | Type | Builder | Built |
|----|------|------|---------|-------|
| 3 | Buffalo Bill | S/O 2-8-0PH | A Bimpson | 1984 |
| | Pixie | 0-4-0PM | J Goulden | 1976 |
| | Norton Priory School | 4w-4PH | Norton Priory School | 1980 |
| | Geraldine | 0-4-0PH | ICI Widnes | 1984 |

# HANDFORTH MODEL ENGINEERING SOCIETY

Building still in progress. The first phase is a simple circuit in a public park. The locomotives listed are the main club locos that run on the track and include two privately owned locos. The circuit is a kidney shaped loop and encloses the raised level track under construction. Handforth is a very new club and as such facilities are still basic; the club would aspire to running at least once a week in the summer but cannot as yet guarantee it, hence anyone wishing to ride or run would be best to contact the club in the first instance.

**Address:** Meriton Road Park, Handforth, Stockport, Cheshire, SK9 3HB.
**Telephone:** 01625 524 750 (Evenings).
**OS Grid Ref:** SJ 856837
**Operator:** Handforth Model Engineering Society.
**Gauge:** 5 inch/7¼ inch.
**Line Length:** 300 yards, circuit.
**First Opened:** Due to open in 2012.

| No | Name | Type | Builder | Built |
|----|------|------|---------|-------|
| | | 0-4-0 | J Simon | 2000 |
| 47632 | | 6-6wPH | B Lomas | 1995 |
| | | 0-6-0BE | D Jeavons | 2009 |

# HAPPY MOUNT EXPRESS

A simple but long established line in the grounds of Happy Mount Park, featuring one station and a tunnel.

**Address:** Happy Mount Park, Bare, Morecambe, Lancashire, LA4 5AQ.
**Telephone:** 01524 582 808.
**OS Grid Ref:** SD 456653.
**Operator:** P Woodhouse.
**Website:** www.happymountpark.co.uk
**Gauge:** 10¼ inch.
**Line Length:** 200 yards, circular.
**First Opened:** c1956.

| No | Name | Type | Builder | Built |
|----|------|------|---------|-------|
| | | 4-4wDH | Northern Hydraulics | 2000 |

# HIGH LEGH RAILWAY

This circuit runs through the grounds of a popular garden centre. Rides are £1 for all.

**Address:** High Legh Garden Centre, Halliwells Brow, Cheshire, WA16 0QW.
**Telephone:** 07799 118 968.
**OS Grid Ref:** ST 700836.
**Operator:** Vee Limited.
**Website:** www.cheshirerailways.co.uk/highlegh
**Gauge:** 7¼ inch.
**Line Length:** 850 yards, circular.
**First Opened:** 2009.

| No | Name | Type | Builder | Built |
|----|------|------|---------|-------|
| | Ella Rose | 0-4-0ST | G May | 1991 |
| | Wren | S/O 0-4-0BE | A Bimpson | 1993 |
| 2006 | Canadian Pacific | 4w-4wBE | A Thatcher | 2006 |
| 641 | Bernina Express | 4-4wBE | G Forman | 2008 |
| | Don | 4wPE | C Edmonson | 2010 |
| | Franklin | 4w-4wBE | A Higgins/I Moore | 2010 |
| | Prince | 4w-4wBE | A Higgins/I Moore | 2011 |
| | Dorothy | 0-4-0BE | A Higgins | 2012 |
| | Samantha | 4w-4wBE | G Forman/A Higgins | 2012 |

▲ New build "Franklin" is seen at the High Legh Railway in Cheshire on 23 May 2010. **Dave Holroyde**

# KNOWSLEY SAFARI PARK RAILWAY

This line forms one of the amusement attractions adjacent to the entrance to the Safari Park. Trains cross a bridge then run alongside a lake to a sharply curved balloon loop. Upon their return another tight loop is traversed to reach the station platform.

**Address:** Knowsley Safari Park, Knowsley Hall, Prescot, Knowsley, Merseyside, L34 4AN.
**Telephone:** 0151 430 9009.
**OS Grid Ref:** SJ 460936.
**Operator:** The Earl of Derby.
**Website:** www.knowsleysafariexperience.co.uk
**Gauge:** 15 inch.
**Line Length:** 800 yards, dumb-bell.
**First Opened:** 1971.

Park entry fee.

| No | Name | Type | Builder | Built |
|----|------|------|---------|-------|
| | | S/O 2-6-0DH | Severn Lamb | 1991 |

# LAKESIDE MINIATURE RAILWAY

One of the two oldest lines in the UK, the Lakeside Miniature Railway can claim a continuous record of service since it was opened originally by Mr Llewellyn, a local postman and shop owner. Trains run from Pleasureland station parallel to the Marine Lake, then curve round underneath the pier to reach Marine Parade. Both terminals have two platforms with their own run-round loops.

**Address:** Marine Lake, Southport, Merseyside, PR8 1RX.
**Telephone:** 01772 745 511.
**OS Grid Ref:** SD 330174.
**Operator:** D Clark & G Leeming.
**Website:** www.lakesideminiaturerailway.co.uk
**Gauge:** 15 inch.
**Line Length:** 750 yards, end to end.
**First Opened:** 1911.

| No | Name | Type | Builder | Built |
|----|------|------|---------|-------|
| 2510 | Prince Charles | S/O 4-6-2DH | H Barlow | 1951 |
| | Golden Jubilee 1911–1961 | S/O 4-6-0DE | H Barlow | 1963 |
| 3 | Jenny | S/O 2-6-2DH | A Moss | 2006 |
| | Princess Anne | 6-6wDH | Severn Lamb | 1971 |

# LANCASTER & MORECAMBE MODEL ENGINEERING SOCIETY

The line is located in a landscaped former quarry and the society formerly had a track at Steamtown, Carnforth.

**Address:** Cinderbarrow Railway, Cinderbarrow Quarry, Tarn Lane, Burton in Kendal, Near Carnforth, Lancashire, LA5 9RX.
**OS Grid Ref:** SD 513758.
**Operator:** Lancaster & Morecombe Model Engineering Society Ltd.
**Website:** www.bumpkinworld.co.uk
**Gauge:** 3½ inch/5 inch/7¼ inch.
**Line Length:** 400 yards, circuit.
**First Opened:** 1998.

| No | Name | Type | Builder | Built |
|----|------|------|---------|-------|
| 6 | Syndy | 0-4-0WT+T | Mulholland/Newsham/Wild | 1991 |
| | Deirdre Jean | 0-4-0ST | K Hodgson | 2000 |
| | Cumbria | 0-6-0ST | S Jackson | 2000 |
| | | 0-4-0ST+T | Mulholland/Wild | 2002 |
| | | 0-6-0T | Mulholland/Wild | 2002 |
| | Cygnet | 0-4-2T | | c2002 |
| | Woodthorpe | 0-6-0BE | Compass House | 1999 |
| D3972 | Tregoss | 0-6-0BE | Compass House | 1999 |

# LITTLE HODDY RAILWAY

Trains run from Little Hoddy station around this circuit, which is a sort of irregular rectangle.

**Address:** Port Haverigg Holiday Village, Near Millom, Cumbria, LA18 4HB.
**Telephone:** 01229 772 880.
**OS Grid Ref:** SD 171788.
**Operator:** R & S Attwood.
**Website:** www.butterflowers.net
**Gauge:** 7¼ inch.
**Line Length:** 400 yards, circular.
**First Opened:** 1997.

| No | Name | Type | Builder | Built |
|---|---|---|---|---|
| | | 0-4-2T | CSM Engineering Services | 1997 |
| | | 4wBE | P Ross | c2001 |
| | | 4wPM | V Crossman | |

# MERSEYSIDE LIVE STEAM & MODEL ENGINEERS

A small circuit in a public park. There is also an elevated 3½ inch/5 inch gauge track.

**Address:** Calderstones Park, Harthill Road, Allerton, Liverpool, Merseyside, L18 3HU.
**OS Grid Ref:** SJ 402876.
**Operator:** Merseyside Live Steam.
**Website:** www.merseysidelivesteam.co.uk
**Gauge:** 5 inch/7¼ inch.
**Line Length:** 150 yards, circular.
**First Opened:** c1950.

▲ 3 "River Irt" enters Ravenglass station with a full train after complete a journey on the 7½ mile Ravenglass & Eskdale Railway on 10 October 2009. **Dave Holroyde**

# PLEASURE BEACH EXPRESS

Ever-popular among the rides at the Blackpool Pleasure Beach is the miniature railway, which wends its way past a lake and among the foundations for numerous other rides.

**Address:** Pleasure Beach, South Shore, Blackpool, Lancashire, FY4 1EZ.
**Telephone:** 0871 222 1234.
**OS Grid Ref:** SD 306333.
**Operator:** Blackpool Pleasure Beach.
**Website:** www.blackpoolpleasurebeach.com
**Gauge:** 21 inch.
**Line Length:** 1000 yards, circular.
**First Opened:** 1934.

Site entry fee.

| No | Name | Type | Builder | Built |
|----|------|------|---------|-------|
| 4472 | Mary Louise | S/O 4-6-2DH | Hudswell Clarke | 1933 |
| 4473 | Carol Jean | S/O 4-6-4DH | Hudswell Clarke | 1933 |
| 6200 | Geoffrey Thompson OBE | S/O 4-6-2DH | Hudswell Clarke | 1935 |
| | Barbie | 4wDM | A Keef | 1982 |

# POT PLACE GARDEN CENTRE RAILWAY

This short line in a garden centre is the only public operating Triang line in the country.

**Address:** The Pot Place, Station Yard, Plumpton, Near Penrith, Cumbria, CA11 9PA.
**Telephone:** 01768 885 500.
**OS Grid Ref:** NY 487370.
**Operator:** The Pot Place.
**Website:** www.thepotplace.co.uk
**Gauge:** 10¼ inch.
**Line Length:** 50 yards, end to end.
**First Opened:** 2009.

| No | Name | Type | Builder | Built |
|----|------|------|---------|-------|
| E5026 | Golden Arrow | 4w-4wBE | Triang | c1963 |

# RAVENGLASS & ESKDALE RAILWAY

The Ravenglass & Eskdale Railway is justifiably marketed as "The most beautiful train journey in England". The line was originally 3 foot gauge but reopened to 15 inch gauge in 1914. It was nearly scrapped in 1960, but was saved at the last moment by a group of enthusiasts and since then has been improved out of all recognition by dedicated permanent staff and volunteers. The railway's workshops have extensive facilities and two locomotives have been built here for a railway in Japan. "Scooter" is being restored off site.

**Address:** Ravenglass, Cumbria, CA18 1SW.
**Telephone:** 01229 717 171.
**OS Grid Ref:** SD 086964.
**Operator:** Ravenglass & Eskdale Railway Co Ltd.
**Website:** www.ravenglass-railway.co.uk
**Gauge:** 15 inch.
**Line Length:** 7 miles, end to end.
**First Opened:** 1876.

| No | Name | Type | Builder | Built |
|----|------|------|---------|-------|
| 3 | River Irt | 0-8-2 | A Heywood | 1894 |
| | Katie | 0-4-0T | A Heywood | 1896 |
| 11 | Bonnie Dundee | 0-4-2 | Kerr Stuart | 1901 |
| | Synolda | 4-4-2 | Bassett Lowke | 1912 |
| 6 | River Esk | 2-8-2 | Davey Paxman | 1923 |
| 9 | River Mite | 2-8-2 | H Clarkson | 1966 |
| 10 | Northern Rock | 2-6-2 | R&ER Co | 1976 |
| | The Flower of the Forest | 2w-2VBT | R&ER Co | 1985 |

| | | | | |
|---|---|---|---|---|
| ICL No1 | | 4-4wPM | Ravenglass | 1925 |
| | Quarryman | 4wPM | Muir Hill | 1926 |
| | Perkins | 4w-4DM | Muir Hill | 1929 |
| ICL9 | Cyril | 4wDM | Lister | 1932 |
| (U2) | | 4wBE | Greenwood & Batley | 1957 |
| 21 | Les | 4wDM | Lister Blackstone | 1960 |
| | Shelagh of Eskdale | 4-6-4DH | Severn Lamb | 1969 |
| 1 | Scooter | 2-2wPMR | R&ER Co | 1970 |
| ICL8 | Lady Wakefield | 4w-4wDH | R&ER Co | 1980 |
| ICL11 | Douglas Ferreira | 4w-4wDH | TMA Engineering | 2005 |

# SAFARI RAILWAY

An out and back run from a terminus next to a small lake.

**Address:** South Lakes Wild Animal Park, Dalton in Furness, Cumbria, LA15 8JR.
**Telephone:** 01229 466 086.
**OS Grid Ref:** SD 238751.
**Operator:** South Lakes Wild Animal Park Ltd.
**Website:** www.wildanimalpark.co.uk
**Gauge:** 7¼ inch.
**Line Length:** 200 yards, end to end.
**First Opened:** 1995.

Park entry fee

| No | Name | Type | Builder | Built |
|---|---|---|---|---|
| | Gillaura | 0-4-0ST+T | A Hall | 1981 |
| 2011 | | 4w-4wDH | L A Services | 2011 |

▲ The R Greatrex "Bagnall" locomotive hauls trains adjacent to farm paddocks on the Silloth Miniature Railway. Here it is seen at the station on 15 September 2011. **Peter Bryant**

# SILLOTH MINIATURE RAILWAY

Located in the corner of Solway Holiday Village, and running through farm paddocks. The journey begins at the station, which is situated next to the farm building. Trains then run down to the bottom of the site where deer are situated, returning via a loop.

**Address:** Solway Holiday Village, Skinburness Drive, Silloth, Cumbria, CA7 4QQ.
**Telephone:** 01697 331 236.
**OS Grid Ref:** NY 118549.
**Operator:** Hagans Leisure Ltd.
**Website:** www.hagansleisure.co.uk
**Gauge:** 7¼ inch.
**Line Length:** 400 yards, dumb-bell.
**First Opened:** 2002.

| No | Name | Type | Builder | Built |
|----|------|------|---------|-------|
| | | 6wPH | R Greatrex | 2001 |

# ST ANNES MINIATURE RAILWAY

This line is more or less rectangular, running through the sand dunes, with the tunnel/stock shed at the back of the circuit.

**Address:** Seafront, St Annes, Lancashire.
**Telephone:** 07772 547 431.
**OS Grid Ref:** SD 322282.
**Operator:** St Annes Miniature Railway Ltd.
**Website:** www.stannesminiaturerailway.co.uk
**Gauge:** 10¼ inch.
**Line Length:** 700 yards, circuit.
**First Opened:** 1973.

| No | Name | Type | Builder | Built |
|----|------|------|---------|-------|
| | Harry's Dream | S/O 2-8-0DH | A Moss | 2005 |
| | St Annes Express | 4w-4PH | Severn Lamb | 1973 |

# WINDMILL ANIMAL FARM RAILWAY

This line runs from the farm to a picnic area at Lakeview. Rapid progress has been made in building the railway, restoring items of rolling stock, and adding covered space to store the ever growing collection. Public access is occasionally possible to the tracks leading from the new turntable, where it is intended to establish a museum section titled "The 15 Inch Gauge Heritage Centre."

**Address:** Windmill Animal Farm, Red Cat Lane, Burscough, Lancashire, L40 1UQ.
**Telephone:** 01704 892 282.
**OS Grid Ref:** SD 427156.
**Operator:** A Moss.
**Website:** www.windmillanimalfarm.co.uk
**Gauge:** 15 inch.
**Line Length:** 750 yards, end to end.
**First Opened:** 1997.

Farm entry fee.

| No | Name | Type | Builder | Built |
|----|------|------|---------|-------|
| | Blue Pacific | 4-6-2 | N Guinness | 1935 |
| | Katie | 2-4-2 | G&SLE | 1956 |
| | Sian | 2-4-2 | G&SLE | 1963 |
| | Red Dragon | 4-4-2 | A Moss/G Walker | 1991 |
| | | 4-4-2 | A Moss | U/C |
| 42869 | | 2-6-0 | C.Gibbons | U/C |
| | Princess Anne | S/O 4-6w-2DE | H Barlow | 1948 |

|  | Duke of Edinburgh | S/O 4-6-2DE | H Barlow | 1950 |
|---|---|---|---|---|
| 4468 | Duke of Edinburgh | S/O 4-6-2DH | H Barlow | 1956 |
|  | Black Smoke | S/O 2-4-2PM | E Smith | c1956 |
|  | Konigswinter | S/O 2-8-2DH | Severn Lamb/CCLR | 1972 |
| 2870 | City of London | S/O 4-6-0DM | Jubilee/Volante | 1987 |
| 5305 |  | S/O 4-6-0BE | A Moss | 1999 |
|  | Whippit Quick | 4w-4DM | Lister | 1935 |
|  | Gwril | 4wDM | Lister | 1943 |
|  |  | 4w-4wDH | G&SLE | 1957 |
| 14 |  | 2w-2PM | G Walker | 1985 |
|  |  | 2-2wPMR | A Moss | 1989 |
|  |  | 4wDE | C Gluyas/D Madden | 2012 |

# WIRRAL MODEL ENGINEERING SOCIETY

There is a 3½ inch/5 inch gauge elevated track here as well as a 7¼ inch gauge ground track. Part of the circuit is double track and there is a maximum gradient of 1 in 60. The loco is turned on a turntable on each trip.

**Address:** Royden Park, Frankby, Wirral, Merseyside, CH48 1NP.
**Telephone:** 0151 648 2967 (Evenings).
**OS Grid Ref:** SJ 247858.
**Operator:** Wirral MES.
**Website:** www.wirralmodelengineeringsociety.co.uk
**Gauge:** 7¼ inch.
**Line Length:** 750 yards, complex.
**First Opened:** 2000.

| No | Name | Type | Builder | Built |
|---|---|---|---|---|
|  | Jasper | 0-4-0ST | BSC/J Jones | 2000 |
|  | Peter George | 0-4-4T | F Stephen | 2007 |
|  | Lets Rumble | 0-4-4T | F Stephen | 2007 |
|  |  | 0-6-0T+T | A Pennell | U/C |
|  | Coolum | 0-6-0T+T | F Stephen | U/C |
| No.1 | Ashover | 4wPH | J Brotherton | 1998 |
|  | Royden | 0-4-0PH | Roanoke | 1999 |
|  | Little Cliffy | 0-4-0PH | Roanoke | 2000 |
|  |  | 4wBE | A Banks | 2009 |

▲ 1933 "Poseidon" is seen in summer sunshine at Scalby Mills station on the 20 inch gauge North Bay Railway in Scarborough. **Peter Bryant**

▼ 1007 "Lynn Mhari" is one of many examples of steam traction at the Thornes Park Miniature Railway in Wakefield. Here it waits to leave the station on 8 March 2008. **Peter Bryant**

# AREA 8: NORTH EAST

County Durham, Northumberland, Tyne & Wear, Yorkshire.

## BRADFORD MODEL ENGINEERING SOCIETY

This line is situated in a woodland park with steaming bays adjacent to the three-road station. The track is dog-bone shaped with interesting gradients.

**Address:** Northcliffe Woods, Cliffe Wood Avenue, Shipley, Bradford, West Yorkshire, BD18 3DD.
**OS Grid Ref:** SE 142366.
**Operator:** Bradford Model Engineering Society.
**Website:** www.bradfordmes.co.uk
**Gauge:** 5 inch/7¼ inch.
**Line Length:** 660 yards, circular.
**First Opened:** 1992.

## CITY OF SUNDERLAND MES

An elevated track in a public park near the seafront. There is also an adjacent elevated track for 3½ inch/5 inch gauge locomotives.

**Address:** Roker Park, Roker, Sunderland, Tyne & Wear.
**Telephone:** 01429 299 649 (Evenings).
**OS Grid Ref:** NZ 405592.
**Operator:** City of Sunderland Model Engineering Society.
**Website:** www.csmes.co.uk
**Gauge:** 5 inch/7¼ inch.
**Line Length:** 300 yards, circular.
**First Opened:** 1981.

| No | Name | Type | Builder | Built |
|---|---|---|---|---|
| | Simplicity | 4wBE | Maxitrak/Sunderland MES | 1989 |
| | Roker Park | 4wBE | City of Sunderland MES | 2002 |
| | | 4w-4wBE | N Maw | c2007 |

## HEATHERSLAW LIGHT RAILWAY

This railway runs from the Old Forge along the banks of the River Till past fields and woodland to terminate below the ruins of Etal Castle. Trains depart hourly, and are normally steam hauled, daily from Easter to the end of October. Please note that "The Lady Augusta" will not be available for service throughout the 2012 season as she will be undertaking necessary boiler repair work.

**Address:** Ford Forge, Heatherslaw, Cornhill on Tweed, Northumberland, TD12 4TJ.
**Telephone:** 01890 820 244.
**OS Grid Ref:** NT 933385.
**Operator:** Heatherslaw Light Rly Co Ltd.
**Website:** www.heatherslawlightrailway.co.uk
**Gauge:** 15 inch.
**Line Length:** 2 miles, end to end.
**First Opened:** 1989.

| No | Name | Type | Builder | Built |
|---|---|---|---|---|
| | The Lady Augusta | 0-4-2 | B Taylor | 1989 |
| | Bunty | 2-6-0T+T | HLR/Alan Keef | 2010 |
| | Clive | 4-4wDH | N Smith | 2000 |

# HEMSWORTH WATER PARK MINIATURE RAILWAY

This line has one station, with a spur to a turntable and a three-road shed. A trip is two circuits.

**Address:** Hemsworth Water Park, Hoyle Mill Road, Kinsley, Near Pontefract, West Yorkshire, WF9 5JB.
**Telephone:** 01977 617 617.
**OS Grid Ref:** SE 425144.
**Operator:** Hemsworth Town Council.
**Website:** www.hemsworthtowncouncil.co.uk/waterpark
**Gauge:** 7¼ inch.
**Line Length:** 300 yards, circular.
**First Opened:** 1993.

Park entry fee.

| No | Name | Type | Builder | Built |
|----|------|------|---------|-------|
| | Mr Sunshine | S/O 4w-4BE | J Pinder | 2008 |
| | Sam | S/O 4w-2BE | J Pinder | 2009 |

▲ 2-6-0T+T "Bunty" is seen with its rake of 8 coaches at Etal Station on the Heatherslaw Light Railway in Northumberland on 3 July 2010.                **Dave Holroyde**

▲ Gala day at the Kirklees Light Railway sees steam workhorses "Fox" and "Badger" double-heading services along the former Clayton West branch. Here they await their next duty on 9 September 2011. **Dave Holroyde**

▼ Sporting a distinctive livery sponsored by main line train operating company Grand Central, "Countess De Grey" waits with a rake of carriages at the Newby Hall Railway on 1 August 2010. **Dave Holroyde**

# HUDDERSFIELD SOCIETY OF MODEL ENGINEERS

The park in which the line operates was the subject of a major improvement scheme in 2010.

**Address:** Greenhead Park, Huddersfield, West Yorkshire, HD1 4DT.
**OS Grid Ref:** SE 134170.
**Operator:** Huddersfield Society of Model Engineers.
**Website:** www.hsme.me.uk
**Gauge:** 5 inch/7¼ inch.
**Line Length:** 600 yards, circular.
**First Opened:** 2001.

| No | Name | Type | Builder | Built |
|----|------|------|---------|-------|
| | Golden Jubilee | 0-4-2 | Holsett Engineering | 2003 |
| | Walrus | 4-4w-4BER | J Pinder | 2001 |
| | The Spirit of Syngenta | 0-4-0PH | Roanoke | 2002 |
| | Blacknight | 0-4-0PH | Roanoke | 2002 |

# HULL AND DISTRCT MODEL ENGINEERING SOCIETY

There is a 2½ inch/3½ inch/5 inch gauge elevated track here in this public park, as well as a ground level track.

**Address:** West Park, Anlaby Road, Hull, East Yorkshire, HU3 6JP.
**OS Grid Ref:** TA 075290.
**Operator:** Hull & District Model Engineering Society.
**Website:** www.finnaj.karoo.net/hdsmee.html
**Gauge:** 3½ inch/5 inch/7¼ inch.
**Line Length:** 450 yards, circular.
**First Opened:** 1994.

| No | Name | Type | Builder | Built |
|----|------|------|---------|-------|
| | Wren | 0-4-0ST | | |
| | | S/O 0-6-0PH | | |

# KIRKLEES LIGHT RAILWAY

This line has been built to recreate the atmosphere of a busy little branch line. Running from Clayton West along a standard gauge trackbed, the railway goes to Shelley, and includes a ¼ mile tunnel. There is also a 5 inch/7¼ inch gauge raised track at Clayton West.

**Address:** Park Mill Way, Long Lane, Clayton West, West Yorkshire, HD8 9XJ.
**Telephone:** 01484 865 727.
**OS Grid Ref:** SE 259112.
**Operator:** Stately Albion T/A Kirklees Light Railway.
**Website:** www.kirkleeslightrailway.com
**Gauge:** 15 inch.
**Line Length:** 3¼ miles, end to end.
**First Opened:** 1991.

| No | Name | Type | Builder | Built |
|----|------|------|---------|-------|
| | Fox | 2-6-2T | B Taylor | 1990 |
| | Badger | 0-6-4ST | B Taylor | 1991 |
| | Hawk | 0-4-0+0-4-0 | B Taylor | 1998 |
| 4 | Owl | 4w-4wTG | B Taylor | 2000 |
| 7 | | S/O 2-2wPH | B Taylor | 1991 |
| | Jay | 4wDH | B Taylor | 1992 |

KATIE ex FAIRBOURNE 242

# LAKESHORE RAILROAD

This line runs around the lake in this public park, with numerous footpath crossings. Both locomotives are notable scale models, "Mountaineer" being 1/6 scale of an Atcheson, Topeka & Santa Fe prototype, and "Adiela" 1/4 scale of a Ferrocarril National del Magdalena (Colombia) locomotive.

**Address:** South Marine Park, South Shields, Tyne & Wear, NE33 2PE.
**Telephone:** 07745 350 983.
**OS Grid Ref:** NZ 373675.
**Operator:** M Henderson.
**Gauge:** 9½ inch.
**Line Length:** 550 yards, circular.
**First Opened:** 1972.

| No | Name | Type | Builder | Built |
|---|---|---|---|---|
| 27 | Adiela | 2-6-2 | Kitson/Bell/Burgoyne | c1939 |
| 3440 | Mountaineer | 4-6-2 | Jennings/Proudlock/Wakefield | 1968 |
| | Rockclimber | 4wPH | M Henderson | 2011 |

# LIGHTWATER EXPRESS

A well engineered line carrying visitors from one side of the park to the other.

**Address:** Lightwater Valley Theme Park, North Stainley, Near Ripon, North Yorkshire, HG4 3HT.
**Telephone:** 0871 720 0011.
**OS Grid Ref:** SE 284758.
**Operator:** Lightwater Leisure Ltd.
**Website:** www.lightwatervalley.co.uk
**Gauge:** 15 inch.
**Line Length:** 1300 yards, circular.
**First Opened:** 1979.

Park entry fee.

| No | Name | Type | Builder | Built |
|---|---|---|---|---|
| 7, 278 | | S/O 2-8-0DH | Severn Lamb | 1984 |

Note: Locomotive carries the number 7 and the number 278.

# NEWBY HALL MINIATURE RAILWAY

Originally an end to end line, built by Cromar White, the line runs in the grounds of Newby Hall Estate near Ripon. Now extended, track runs parallel to the River Ure in the shape of a dumb-bell loop. The station, Newby Hall, is situated in the middle of the line and has a turntable and engine shed. Locomotives used on the railway are two Severn Lamb locomotives or a Battison built "Royal Scot" which has run here since the line was constructed and has been recently overhauled.

**Address:** Newby Hall & Gardens, Ripon, North Yorkshire, HG4 5AE.
**Telephone:** 0845 450 4068.
**OS Ref:** SE 347675.
**Operator:** Newby Hall & Gardens.
**Website:** www.newbyhallandgardens.com
**Gauge:** 10¼ inch.
**Line Length:** 1000 yards, dumb-bell.
**First opened:** 1971.

Site Entry Fee.

| No | Name | Type | Builder | Built |
|---|---|---|---|---|
| 6100 | Royal Scot | 4-6-0 | S.Battison | 1953 |
| D1017 | Lady Mary Vyner | 6-6wGM | Severn Lamb | 1970 |
| | Countess de Grey | 4w-4GH | Severn Lamb | 1973 |

# NORTH BAY RAILWAY

Trains depart from Peasholm station, dive beneath the water chute and through a short tunnel, before swinging out to gain the sea front at the half way passing loop, whence they continue to Scalby Mills. There is now a turntable at Scalby Mills, but at Peasholm locomotives run round and turn by means of a sharply curved loop. A professionally run line performing a useful task in transporting visitors to and from the attractions at Scalby Mills.

**Address:** Northstead Manor Gardens, Scarborough, North Yorkshire, YO12 6PF.
**Telephone:** 01723 368 791.
**OS Grid Ref:** TA 035898.
**Operator:** North Bay Railway Company Ltd.
**Website:** www.nbr.org.uk
**Gauge:** 20 inch.
**Line Length:** 1300 yards, end to end.
**First Opened:** 1931.

| No | Name | Type | Builder | Built |
|---|---|---|---|---|
| 1931 | Neptune | S/O 4-6-2DH | Hudswell Clarke | 1931 |
| 1932 | Triton | S/O 4-6-2DH | Hudswell Clarke | 1932 |
| 570 | Robin Hood | S/O 4-6-4DH | Hudswell Clarke | 1932 |
| 1933 | Poseidon | S/O 4-6-2DH | Hudswell Clarke | 1933 |
| | Georgina    Bagnall replica | 040ST | | 2016 |

▲ North Bay Railway's 1931 "Neptune" & 1932 "Triton", two of the oldest diesel hydraulic locomotives in the world, are seen at Scalby Mills on 16 May 2010.          **Dave Holroyde**

# ORCHARD FARM LAKESIDE RAILWAY

A recently constructed line in the grounds of this caravan park. It boasts an attractive station with overall roof, from where trains head out and around the lake.

**Address:** Orchard Farm Holiday Village, Hunmanby, North Yorkshire, YO14 0PU.
**Telephone:** 01723 891 582.
**OS Grid Ref:** TA 104778.
**Operator:** Mr Dugdale.
**Website:** www.orchardfarmholidayvillage.co.uk
**Gauge:** 10¼ inch.
**Line Length:** 600 yards, circular.
**First Opened:** 1995.

| No | Name | Type | Builder | Built |
|----|------|------|---------|-------|
| | Glanllyn | 0-4-4T | Dugdale/Plumber/GNS | U/C |
| | Orchard Flyer | 6w-6wDM | R Yates | 1979 |
| | Humanby Flyer | 4wDH | A Hunnybell | 2002 |

# PUGNEYS LIGHT RAILWAY

The line runs from Pugneys Lakeside along the edge of the lake via a passing loop to Pugneys Central, and then around a balloon loop. The line is currently for sale

**Address:** Pugneys Country Park, Durkar, Wakefield, West Yorkshire, WF2 7EQ.
**Telephone:** 01924 264 385 (Evenings).
**OS Grid Ref:** SE 324179.
**Operator:** J Pinder.
**Website:** www.wakefield.gov.uk
**Gauge:** 7¼ inch.
**Line Length:** 750 yards, balloon loop.
**First Opened:** 1998.

| No | Name | Type | Builder | Built |
|----|------|------|---------|-------|
| | | 4-car BER | J Pinder | 2005 |
| | | 4w-4wPH | J Pinder | 2012 |

# RIO GRANDE MINIATURE RAILWAY

This railway is unique in that its station is situated inside a glasshouse. The journey features a bridge, a tunnel, and two level crossings.

**Address:** Saville Bros Garden Centre, Selby Road, Garforth Cliff, Garforth, Leeds, West Yorkshire, LS25 2AQ.
**Telephone:** 0113 286 2183.
**OS Grid Ref:** SE 416319.
**Operator:** Saville Bros Ltd.
**Website:** www.klondyke.co.uk/savilles-garden-centre-leeds
**Gauge:** 10¼ inch.
**Line Length:** 900 yards, dumb-bell.
**First Opened:** 1978.

| No | Name | Type | Builder | Built |
|----|------|------|---------|-------|
| 278 | | S/O 2-8-0PH | Severn Lamb | 1978 |

▲ "Orchard Flyer" waits at the station of the Orchard Farm Lakeside Railway on 16 May 2010.
**Dave Holroyde**

▼ Railcar motive power is often used at the Pugneys Light Railway near Wakefield. This example, based on a Docklands Light Railway set, is seen working a busy service on 27 July 2008. **Peter Bryant**

▲ Severn Lamb Rio Grande locomotive 278 hauls trains at the Rio Grande Miniature Railway of Saville Bros Garden Centre in Garforth. Here it is seen on a day off in March 2008. **Peter Bryant**

▼ A miniature railway with a difference! Not only are the locomotives at Wolds Way Lavender used for passengers, but also for the transport of lavender around the site. This Roanoke loco is seen on 16 May 2010. **Dave Holroyde**

# ROTHERHAM & DISTRICT MODEL ENGINEERING SOCIETY

There is a 3½ inch/5 inch/7¼ inch gauge elevated track inside the ground level track.

**Address:** Victoria (Rosehill) Park, Rawmarsh, Rotherham, South Yorkshire, S62 7JS.
**OS Grid Ref:** SK 438973.
**Operator:** Rotherham & District Model Engineering Society.
**Website:** www.rdmes.co.uk
**Gauge:** 7¼ inch.
**Line Length:** 300 yards, circular.
**First Opened:** 1998.

# RUSWARP MINIATURE RAILWAY

This line is a convoluted circuit, twisted round upon itself in land adjacent to the River Esk.

**Address:** The Carrs, Ruswarp, Near Whitby, North Yorkshire, YO21 1RL.
**Telephone:** 01947 600 109.
**OS Grid Ref:** NZ 885088.
**Operator:** N Pearson.
**Website:** www.chainbridgeriverside.com
**Gauge:** 7¼ inch.
**Line Length:** 700 yards, circular.
**First Opened:** 1990.

| No | Name | Type | Builder | Built |
|---|---|---|---|---|
| | Stanley | 0-4-2T | J Bailiss | 2007 |
| 20072 | Percy | 4w-4PH | D Oswald | 1992 |

# RYEDALE SOCIETY OF MODEL ENGINEERS

Principally a 5 inch gauge society that concentrates on scale trains, particularly at the twice a year Main Line rallies. The line is double track ("kidney shaped") which is fully signalled and controlled from two signal boxes. There are three sets of sidings for 5 inch rolling stock.

**Address:** The Old School, Pottergate, Gilling East, North Yorkshire, YO62 4JJ.
**OS Grid Ref:** SE 613770.
**Operator:** Ryedale Society of Model Engineers.
**Website:** www.rsme.org.uk
**Gauge:** 3½ inch/5 inch/7¼ inch.
**Line Length:** 400 yards, circular.
**First Opened:** 1983.

# SALTBURN MINIATURE RAILWAY

A long established line running from a coastal terminus at Cat Nab into the Italian Gardens. Its future now seems assured since it was taken over by a group of enthusiasts some years ago.

**Address:** Cat Nab, Saltburn, North Yorkshire, TS12 1HH.
**Telephone:** 07813 153 975.
**OS Grid Ref:** NZ 668215.
**Operator:** Saltburn Miniature Railway Association.
**Website:** www.saltburn-miniature-railway.org.uk
**Gauge:** 15 inch.
**Line Length:** 700 yards, end to end.
**First Opened:** 1947.

| No | Name | Type | Builder | Built |
|---|---|---|---|---|
| | Prince Charles | S/O 4-6-2DE | H Barlow | 1953 |
| | Saltburn 150 | S/O 4-6-2DH | Artisair | 1972 |
| | George Outhwaite | S/O 0-4-0DH | Saltburn Min Rly Assoc | 1994 |

# SHIBDEN MINIATURE RAILWAY

This railway is situated at the valley bottom of a large park that includes a museum in Shibden Hall. The track loops around between a stream and the side of the valley through woodland and a picnic area. There is a tunnel and two bridges over the stream.

**Address:** Shibden Park, Listers Road, Halifax, West Yorkshire, HX3 6XG.
**Telephone:** 07854 658 635.
**OS Grid Ref:** SE 109261.
**Operator:** R Trout.
**Gauge:** 10¼ inch.
**Line Length:** 750 yards, circular.
**First Opened:** 1983.

| No | Name | Type | Builder | Built |
|----|------|------|---------|-------|
| 1 | Ivor | 0-6-0ST | B Taylor | 1984 |
| | Ivan | 4w-4wDE | B Taylor | 1985 |

# SOUTH GARDEN MINIATURE RAILWAY

This line has been laid in the South Yard of the National Railway Museum. The locomotive runs round the train at each end of the recently extended line. There are other miniature railway locomotives and rolling stock available to see in the Warehouse and Great Hall at the museum.

**Address:** National Railway Museum, Leeman Road, York, North Yorkshire, YO26 4XJ.
**Telephone:** 0844 815 3139.
**OS Grid Ref:** SE 593519.
**Operator:** National Railway Museum.
**Website:** www.nrm.org.uk
**Gauge:** 7¼ inch.
**Line Length:** 150 yards, end to end.
**First Opened:** 1996.

| No | Name | Type | Builder | Built |
|----|------|------|---------|-------|
| | Lady Margaret | 0-4-0ST | National Railway Museum | 1981 |
| | John | 6wPH | R Greatrex | 1997 |
| | Helen | 6wPH | R Greatrex | 1998 |
| 55 002 | The King's Own Yorkshire Light Infantry | 6w-6wDH | Mardyke | 2011 |

# TEESSIDE SMALL GAUGE RAILWAY

The line is located in the grounds of Preston Hall Museum. The ground level track has a station and spur to the sheds. The elevated track has been added within the main circuit.

**Address:** Preston Park, Eaglescliffe, County Durham, TS18 3RH.
**Telephone:** 01642 652 675 (Evenings).
**OS Grid Ref:** NZ 429161.
**Operator:** Teeside Small Gauge Railway.
**Website:** www.tsgr.co.uk
**Gauge:** 5 inch/7¼ inch.
**Line Length:** 400 yards, circuit.
**First Opened:** 1995.

| No | Name | Type | Builder | Built |
|----|------|------|---------|-------|
| | Linda | 0-4-0ST+T | S Pearson | 1989 |
| | Preston | 0-6-0T | Teesside SGR | 2012 |
| 7364 | | 4w-4wBE | Teesside SGR | 2000 |
| | Preston Flyer | 4wBE | Phoenix/Teesside SGR | 2004 |

▲ Mardyke Deltic locomotive 55 002 "The Kings Own Yorkshire Light Infantry" prepares to leave for the 200 yard journey around the South Gardens at the National Railway Museum in York on 24 September 2011. **Dave Holroyde**

▼ Club built 7364 makes its way round the track on the Teeside Small Gauge Railway on 17 April 2011. **Dave Holroyde**

# THORNE MEMORIAL PARK MINIATURE RAILWAY

A ground level multi-gauge track in a public park.

**Address:** Thorne Memorial Park, Thorne, South Yorkshire, DN8 5DZ.
**OS Grid Ref:** SE 687130.
**Operator:** Doncaster & District Model Engineering Society Ltd.
**Website:** www.thornerailway.co.uk
**Gauge:** 5 inch/7¼ inch.
**Line Length:** 200 yards, circuit.
**First Opened:** 1998.

# THORNES PARK RAILWAY

This line is a circle wrapped across itself, by means of a diamond crossing. It has an impressive stable of motive power. Trains run on Saturday and Sunday afternoons.

**Address:** Thornes Park, Lawefield Lane, Wakefield, West Yorkshire, WF2 8QE.
**Telephone:** 07779 601 180 (Evenings).
**OS Grid Ref:** SE 323201.
**Operator:** Wakefield Society of Model and Experimental Engineers.
**Gauge:** 7¼ inch.
**Line Length:** 800 yards, complex.
**First Opened:** c1974.

| No | Name | Type | Builder | Built |
|----|------|------|---------|-------|
| | Linda | 0-4-0ST | J Stubbs | 1978 |
| 1007 | Lynn Mhari | 4-8-4 | J Stubbs | 1988 |
| 70008 | Black Prince | 4-6-2 | A Bickerstaffe | 1989 |
| | Hiawatha | 4-6-4 | J Stubbs/I Hickling | 1997 |
| 417 | General Palmer | 2-8-0 | J Stubbs/A Bickerstaffe | 2003 |
| | Jeff | 0-4-2T | J Stubbs | 2005 |
| E762 | Lyn | 2-4-2T | Winson/J Bailiss | 2005 |
| 2510 | | 6w-6wPH | J Stubbs/D Phillips | 1986 |
| | Edith | 4w-2DH | J Horsfield | 1990 |
| D9013 | The Black Watch | 6w-6wPH | A Bickerstaffe | 2009 |

# TYNESIDE SOCIETY OF MODEL ENGINEERS

There is an elevated track here and 7¼ inch gauge locomotives from here also run at Beamish Model Engineering Group, Beamish Museum on certain days a year. No locomotives here are stored on site.

**Address:** Exhibition Park, Town Moor, Newcastle upon Tyne, Tyne & Wear, NE2 4AA.
**OS Grid Ref:** NZ 246659.
**Operator:** Tyneside Society of Model & Experimental Engineers.
**Website:** www.tsmee.co.uk
**Gauge:** 5 inch/7¼ inch.
**Line Length:** 200 yards, circular.
**First Opened:** 2010.

| No | Name | Type | Builder | Built |
|----|------|------|---------|-------|
| | Imp | 0-4-0ST | D & M Holt | 1990 |
| | Belmont | 0-6-0ST | A Bones | 1990 |
| | Nathan | 0-4-0ST | E Ions | 2008 |

# WEST RIDING SMALL LOCOMOTIVE SOCIETY

The circuit here has an elevated track just inside it; there is a tunnel just before the station.

**Address:** Blackgates, Bradford Road, Tingley, Near Wakefield, West Yorkshire, WF3 1RU.
**OS Grid Ref:** SE 291261.
**Operator:** West Riding Small Locomotive Society Ltd.
**Website:** https://sites.google.com/a/wrsls.com/www/home
**Gauge:** 7¼ inch.
**Line Length:** 250 yards, circular.
**First Opened:** 1986.

# WOLDS WAY LAVENDER RAILWAY

As well as carrying the public, this little line is also used to carry lavender from the fields to the processing plant.

**Address:** Wintringham, Near Malton, North Yorkshire, YO17 8HW.
**Telephone:** 01944 758 641.
**OS Grid Ref:** SE 874744.
**Operator:** Wolds Way Lavender.
**Website:** www.woldswaylavender.co.uk
**Gauge:** 7¼ inch.
**Line Length:** 550 yards, end to end.
**First Opened:** 2005.

| No | Name | Type | Builder | Built |
|---|---|---|---|---|
| | Sarah Anne | 0-4-0ST+T | S Jacques | U/C |
| | | 0-4-0PH | Roanoke | 2005 |

# WORTLEY FORGE MINIATURE RAILWAY

This line is a long thin circuit, situated in idyllic countryside between the forge and the River Don. The station at Wortley Central is broadly in the middle. Part of the track is interlaced with a 15 inch gauge industrial line. Forge Halt Station at the downstream end of the line provides easy access to the Top Forge Industrial Museum.

**Address:** Wortley Top Forge, Wortley, Near Stocksbridge, South Yorkshire, S35 7DN.
**Telephone:** 01226 728 423.
**OS Grid Ref:** SK 295999.
**Operator:** Wortley Top Forge Model Engineers Society.
**Website:** www.wortleymes.com
**Gauge:** 5 inch/7¼ inch.
**Line Length:** 600 yards, dog-bone.
**First Opened:** 1980.

| No | Name | Type | Builder | Built |
|---|---|---|---|---|
| | Bethany | 0-4-0 | Pratt/Oughton | 1978 |
| | Emily | 0-4-0 | Pettifer/Walton | 1979 |
| | Wild Aster | 0-4-0ST+T | C Farrar | 1993 |
| | Mythago | 0-4-0ST+T | S Hazlewood | 1999 |
| | Cackler | 0-4-0ST | C Farrar | 2000 |
| | | 0-4-0ST | D Smith | 2009 |
| 2049 | | 4w-4wBER | A Butteriss | 1997 |
| 55 | | 4wBE | Express/Ripley | 2002 |
| 20147 | | 4w-4wBER | Wortley Top Forge MES | 2010 |

# AREA 9: SCOTLAND

## AGNEW PARK MINIATURE RAILWAY

The railway is situated at the busy sea port of Stranraer and follows contours around the boating lake, crazy golf course and children's playground, with a station adjacent to the Agnew Park Pavilion. There is a spur to a turntable and a four-road shed. The location has extensive sea views down Loch Ryan to Ailsa Craig and Arran. The locomotive pulls two Knightley Light Railway sit-astride carriages.

**Address:** Agnew Park, Seafront, Stranraer, Dumfries & Galloway, DG9 7JZ.
**Telephone:** 01776 702 151.
**OS Grid Ref:** NX 056612.
**Operator:** Dumfries and Galloway Council.
**Website:** www.dgcommunity.net
**Gauge:** 7¼ inch.
**Line Length:** 800 yards, circular.
**First Opened:** 1997.

| No | Name | Type | Builder | Built |
|----|------|------|---------|-------|
|    |      | 6wPH | R Greatrex | 1997 |

▲ D7594 "Angus" waits between duties at the world's oldest 10¼ inch gauge miniature railway, Kerr's Miniature Railway at West Links Park, Arbroath.  **Peter Bryant**

# HIGHLAND LIGHT RAILWAY

The railway is used for farm work and for carrying visitors to the local farmers' markets.

**Address:** Mill of Logierait Farm, Pitlochry, Perthshire, PH9 0LH.
**Telephone:** 01796 482 222.
**OS Grid Ref:** NN 971519.
**Operator:** Peter Guinan.
**Website:** www.railwayfarm.com
**Gauge:** 10¼ inch.
**Line Length:** 1380 yards, balloon loop.
**First Opened:** 2011.

| No | Name | Type | Builder | Built |
|----|------|------|---------|-------|
| | Claude the Colonel | S/O 4w-4wDH | P Bowers | 2001 |
| | "Thud Thud" | 2w-2DH | A Moss | 1992 |

# KERR'S MINIATURE RAILWAY

Kerr's Miniature Railway is one of Britain's oldest miniature railways (oldest in Scotland), having carried over 2 million passengers since opening in 1935. It runs up and down for a quarter of a mile adjacent to the East Coast Main Line between Aberdeen and Edinburgh, passing through a tunnel on the way. Now in its third generation, the railway is run by mother and son, Jill & John, who are also provided with lots of help from their team of volunteers. Their straight track is renowned for not having a stone of ballast out of place. Children's rides are also given in a miniature bus and fire engine when the railway is open. An extension here is planned, extending the railway into the centre of West Links Park.

**Address:** West Links Park, Arbroath, Angus, DD11 1QD.
**Telephone:** 01241 879 249.
**OS Grid Ref:** NO 629401.
**Operator:** J & J Kerr.
**Website:** www.kerrsminiaturerailway.co.uk
**Gauge:** 10¼ inch.
**Line Length:** 350 yards, end to end.
**First Opened:** 1935.

| No | Name | Type | Builder | Built |
|----|------|------|---------|-------|
| 3007 | Firefly | 0-6-0 | H Bullock | 1936 |
| 9872 | Auld Reekie | S/O 4-4-2PM | W Jennings | 1935 |
| | Ivor | S/O 0-6-0DM | Coleby Simkins | 1972 |
| 25081 | Elliot | 4-4wPM | M Eastwood | 1981 |
| D7594 | Angus | 4-4wPM | M Eastwood | 1992 |

# NESS ISLANDS RAILWAY

Britain's most northerly public miniature railway is situated on the western edge of Inverness, on an island consisting mainly of a children's play park and boating lake. The line is a dumb-bell folded over on top of itself, with the station on the C shaped single line in the middle.

**Address:** Whin Island, Bught Park, Inverness, Inverness-shire, IV3 5SS.
**Telephone:** 01463 235 533.
**OS Grid Ref:** NH 658434.
**Operator:** I Young.
**Website:** www.nessislandsrailway.co.uk
**Gauge:** 7¼ inch.
**Line Length:** 950 yards, dumb-bell.
**First Opened:** 1983.

| No | Name | Type | Builder | Built |
|----|------|------|---------|-------|
| 91001 | Uncle Frank | 4w-4wDH | Mardyke | 1991 |
| 47469 | Uncle John | 6w-6wDH | Mardyke | 2011 |

# STRATHAVEN MINIATURE RAILWAY

This line is a double circuit with the two routes connected by a crossing next to the station. Trains run anti-clockwise from Strathaven Central Station. There is an elevated track within the main circuits.

**Address:** George Allan Park, Three Stones Road, Strathaven, South Lanarkshire, ML10 6EF.
**Telephone:** 01555 892 657 (Evenings).
**OS Grid Ref:** NS 700448.
**Operator:** Strathaven Model Society Ltd.
**Gauge:** 5 inch/7¼ inch.
**Line Length:** 500 yards, circular.
**First Opened:** 1949.

| No | Name | Type | Builder | Built |
|----|------|------|---------|-------|
| 1949 | Margaret | 2-6-0 | Scott/Hamilton | 1947 |
| 77020 | | 2-6-0 | D Horsfall | 1984 |
| | Eva | 0-4-0ST | C Taylor | c1989 |
| 44700 | | 4-6-0 | K Johnstone | 2000 |
| | Agnes Elder | 0-4-0ST | K Johnstone | 2011 |
| | | 0-4-2T | | |
| | Abberton | 4wPH | Pfeifferbahn | 1992 |
| | | 0-6-0BE | Compass House | 2002 |

# VOGRIE PARK MINIATURE RAILWAY

A multi-gauge ground level club track in a public park.

**Address:** Vogrie Country Park, Dalkeith, Midlothian, EH23 4NZ.
**Telephone:** 01875 822 388.
**OS Grid Ref:** NT 377631.
**Operator:** Eskvalley Model Engineering Society.
**Website:** www.vpmr.org.uk
**Gauge:** 3½ inch/5 inch/7¼ inch.
**Line Length:** 650 yards, circular.
**First Opened:** 1986.

| No | Name | Type | Builder | Built |
|----|------|------|---------|-------|
| | Kate | 0-6-2T | J Hawker | 1976 |
| | | 4w-4wBE | Eskvalley | |
| | Vogrie Castle | 0-6-0PH | Eskvalley | |
| | Peter D | 0-6-0PM | B Hird | |

111

▲ 4wPH "Abberton" is seen crossing the turntable on a wet day in August 2007 at the Strathaven Miniature Railway.                                                                 **Peter Scott**

▼ Modified Tinkerbell locomotive "Douglas" pauses in the arrival platform of the 7¼ inch gauge line at the Conwy Valley Railway Museum, Betws-y-Coed, on 23 August 2009.     **Dave Holroyde**

# AREA 10: WALES

## CITY OF NEWPORT MODEL ENGINEERS SOCIETY

This site features a 3½ inch and 5 inch gauge elevated track adjacent to the ground level line, which loops around the boating pond and wildlife lakes. The railway is open to the public on the first Saturday of the month, rides given on the ground level track using members' locomotives.

**Address:** St Juliens, North Glebelands, Bank Street, Newport, Gwent, NP19 7HF.
**Telephone:** 07836 534 338 (Evenings).
**OS Grid Ref:** ST 319900.
**Operator:** City of Newport MES.
**Website:** www.newportmes.webplus.net
**Gauge:** 5 inch/7¼ inch.
**Line Length:** Complex.
**First Opened:** 2009.

## CONWY VALLEY RAILWAY

The Conwy Valley Railway Museum can be found over the footbridge from Betws-y-Coed. Within the museum can be found the fine scale model of "Britannia", along with interesting exhibits including other large scale models. Outside the museum is an extensive and ever-popular 7¼ inch gauge railway, basically a dumb-bell layout with the two loops interlaced. The line crosses behind the museum, protected by automatic level crossing barriers. The 15 inch gauge line is worked by an open tram, taking power from an overhead power line using a traditional trolley pole. The 4wBER operates on a separate track; put a coin in the slot and drive your own train. The museum, 7¼ inch gauge line and tramway are complementary attractions, all in a popular location.

**Address:** Conwy Valley Railway Museum, Old Station, Betws-y-Coed, Conwy, LL24 0AL.
**Telephone:** 01690 710 568.
**OS Grid Ref:** SH 796565.
**Operator:** C Cartwright.
**Website:** www.conwyrailwaymuseum.co.uk
**Gauge:** 7¼ inch/15 inch.
**Line Length:** 7¼ inch gauge, 950 yards, complex; 15 inch gauge, 500 yards, end to end.
**First Opened:** 7¼ inch gauge, 1979; 15 inch gauge, 1991.

### 7¼ inch gauge:

| No | Name | Type | Builder | Built |
|----|------|------|---------|-------|
| 402 | Shoshone | 2-8-0 | Milner Engineering | 1977 |
| 407 | Old Rube | 2-8-0 | Milner Engineering | 1983 |
| | Douglas | 0-4-2T | P Frank | 2004 |
| | | 2-6-2+2-6-2 | CVRM | U/C |
| 7 | | S/O 4wBER | Parkside | 1995 |
| 6641 | | 4-4wPH | R Greatrex | 1990 |
| | Gwydir Castle | 4w-4wPH | P Zwicky Ross/CVRM | 2004 |

### 15 inch gauge:

| No | Name | Type | Builder | Built |
|----|------|------|---------|-------|
| 70000 | Britannia | 4-6-2 | Longfleet/TMA | 1988 |
| | | 4w-4wWER | Wall/Cartwright | 1989 |

# DIBLEYS NURSERIES RAILWAY

The line is located within the grounds of this specialist plants nursery.

**Address:** Dibleys Garden Centre, Llanelidan, Ruthin, Denbighshire, LL15 2LG.
**Telephone:** 01978 790 677.
**OS Grid Ref:** SJ 131496.
**Operator:** Dibleys Nurseries.
**Website:** www.dibleys.com
**Gauge:** 7¼ inch.
**Line Length:** 850 yards, complex.
**First Opened:** 2001.

| No | Name | Type | Builder | Built |
|---|---|---|---|---|
| | Cricor | 0-4-2T | Exmoor Steam Railway | 1999 |
| | | 4w-4wBER | RMI Railworks | 2001 |
| | | 4w-4wBER | RMI Railworks | 2003 |

▲ Union Pacific locomotive 6641, built by Roger Greatrex of Knightley Light Railway, is seen working at the Conwy Valley Railway Museum, Betws-y-Coed on 27 August 2009. **Dave Holroyde**

# FAIRBOURNE RAILWAY

This line originated in 1896 as a 2 foot gauge horse tramway. In 1916 the tramway was relaid to 15 inch gauge. In this form the line eked out a humble existence until the mid-1950s when a decade of improvements commenced. In 1984 a new owner took over and the line was progressively transformed, including re-gauging to 12¼ inch in 1986. Trains are now mostly hauled by one of four half-size replicas of 2 foot gauge steam locomotives. The present owners bought the railway in 1995.

The line runs from Fairbourne station alongside Beach Road and through the sand dunes passing Golf Halt. Trains often pass at the mid-way loop, before continuing next to the road, then entering a long tunnel and emerging on the far side of the dunes, finally swinging round into Barmouth Ferry Station. From here it is only a short ferry ride to Barmouth.

**Address:** Beach Road, Fairbourne, Gwynedd, LL38 2EX.
**Telephone:** 01341 250 362.
**OS Grid Ref:** SH 616128.
**Operator:** Fairbourne Railway.
**Website:** www.fairbournerailway.com
**Gauge:** 12¼ inch.
**Line Length:** 1¾ miles, end to end.
**First Opened:** 1916.

| No | Name | Type | Builder | Built |
|----|------|------|---------|-------|
| 4 | Sherpa | 0-4-0ST+T | Milner Engineering | 1978 |
| E759 | Yeo | 2-6-2T | D Curwen | 1978 |
| 5 | Russell | 2-6-4T | Milner Engineering | 1979 |
| 2 | Beddgelert | 0-6-4T | D Curwen | 1979 |
| | Tony | 4w-4wDM | G&SLE | 1961 |
| | Gwril | 4wDH | Hunslet | 1994 |

▲ E759 "Yeo" and 4 "Sherpa" pause at Fairbourne station on the 12¼ inch gauge Fairbourne Railway.
**Peter Bryant**

# LLWYFAN CERRIG MINIATURE RAILWAY

The only public access to this line is by train via the Gwili Railway from Bronwydd Arms station; the 7¼ inch gauge line operates on every day that Gwili trains are timetabled.

**Address:** Llwyfan Cerrig Station, Gwili Railway, Near Carmarthen, Carmarthenshire, SA44 5TD.
**Telephone:** 01267 238 213.
**OS Grid Ref:** SN 405258.
**Operator:** Gwili Railway Ltd.
**Website:** www.gwili-railway.co.uk
**Gauge:** 7¼ inch.
**Line Length:** 250 yards, end to end.
**First Opened:** 1993.

Site entry fee.

| No | Name | Type | Builder | Built |
|----|------|------|---------|-------|
| 1366 | | 0-6-0PT | R Ward | 1998 |
| 1 | | S/O 0-6-0PH | F Bond | 1997 |
| | Ben | 0-4-0PH | Roanoke | 2003 |

# OAKWOOD MINIATURE RAILWAY

This line serves as a transport system from the entrance to the main part of the adventure park. Passengers travel from Oakwood station, serving the entrance, around to Whistlestop station, where they disembark. When leaving the park they return around a much shorter section of the circuit.

**Address:** Oakwood Theme Park, Canaston Bridge, Narberth, Pembrokeshire, SA67 8DE.
**Telephone:** 01834 891 376.
**OS Grid Ref:** SN 069124.
**Operator:** Oakwood Leisure Ltd.
**Website:** www.oakwoodthemepark.co.uk
**Gauge:** 15 inch.
**Line Length:** 1100 yards, circuit.
**First Opened:** 1987.

Park entry fee.

| No | Name | Type | Builder | Built |
|----|------|------|---------|-------|
| | Lindy-Lou | S/O 0-8-0DH | Severn Lamb | 1972 |
| | | S/O 0-8-0PH | Severn Lamb | 1976 |
| | Lenka | 4-4wDHR | Severn Lamb | 1973 |
| | Lorna | 4-4wDHR | Goold Bros | 1989 |

# PORTHMADOG WOODLAND RAILWAY

Located directly next to Gelert's Farm station at the Welsh Highland Heritage Railway, featuring a tunnel, bridge and viaduct, all within the unusual triangular running line.

**Address:** Welsh Highland Heritage Railway, Tremadog Road, Porthmadog, Gwynedd, LL49 9DY.
**Telephone:** 01766 513 402.
**OS Grid Ref:** SH 570392.
**Operator:** R Washington.
**Website:** www.whr.co.uk
**Gauge:** 7¼ inch.
**Line Length:** 500 yards, complex.
**First Opened:** 2005.

| No | Name | Type | Builder | Built |
|----|------|------|---------|-------|
| | Petunia | 0-4-2T | J Stubbs/S Hurley | 1997 |
| 7 | | S/O 4w-4PH | R Washington | 2008 |
| | Deudraeth Castle | 0-6-0PH | R & L Washington | 1995 |
| 8 | | 4wBE | R Washington | 2010 |

# RHYL MINIATURE RAILWAY

This line is the oldest miniature railway in the country, the original line running on the Marine Lake site until 1969, and relaid twice, in 1978 and again in 1998. The station building here was opened in 2007 and holds a museum of the line's history. A Class 10 Bassett Lowke "Little Giant" replica is under construction here.

**Address:** Marine Lake Leisure Park, Wellington Road, Rhyl, Denbighshire, LL18 1AQ.
**Telephone:** 01352 759 109 (Evenings).
**OS Grid Ref:** SH 999807.
**Operator:** Rhyl Steam Preservation Trust.
**Website:** www.rhylminiaturerailway.co.uk
**Gauge:** 15 inch.
**Line Length:** 1 mile, circular.
**First Opened:** 1911.

| No | Name | Type | Builder | Built |
|----|------|------|---------|-------|
| 44 | | 4-4-0 | Cagney | c1910 |
| 101 | Joan | 4-4-2 | A Barnes | 1920 |
| 102 | Railway Queen | 4-4-2 | A Barnes | c1921 |
| 105 | Michael | 4-4-2 | A Barnes | c1927 |
| 106 | Billy | 4-4-2 | A Barnes | c1934 |
| | Clara | S/O 0-4-2DH | G&SLE | 1961 |
| | | 4wDM | Lister | 1938 |
| (3) | | 2w-2-4BER | Hayne/Minirail | 1983 |

# TEIFI VALLEY MINIATURE RAILWAY

This line is an ancillary attraction to the 2 foot gauge trains of the Teifi Valley Railway. Trains run from Henllan high level station.

**Address:** Teifi Valley Railway, Henllan, Near Newcastle Emlyn, Ceredigion, SA44 5TD.
**Telephone:** 01559 371 077.
**OS Grid Ref:** SN 359407.
**Operator:** Teifi Valley Railway.
**Website:** www.teifivalleyrailway.org
**Gauge:** 7¼ inch.
**Line Length:** 300 yards, end to end.
**First Opened:** 1998.

| No | Name | Type | Builder | Built |
|----|------|------|---------|-------|
| | | S/O 0-6-0PH | F Bond | 1998 |

▲ Roanoke locomotive "Ben" prepares to leave Llwyfan Cerrig station on the Llwyfan Cerrig Miniature Railway with a full train on 2 September 2011. **Roy Lambeth**

▼ A Barnes Atlantic double-header! Visiting locomotive John from the Evesham Vale Light Railway leads resident Barnes locomotive Joan on the Rhyl Miniature Railway. **Peter Bryant**

# AREA 11: IRELAND

## BALLYMOTE MINIATURE RAILWAY

This railway runs directly next to the main line railway in the town park, which also houses a playground and 13th century Norman Castle and Franciscan Abbey. Trains are operated by a Roanoke petrol shunter, pulling three Joe Nemeth sit-in carriages.

**Address:** Ballymote Town Park, Ballymote, County Sligo, Irish Republic.
**Telephone:** (+353) 071 918 3992.
**OS Grid Ref:** G 660157.
**Operator:** Ballymote Community Enteprises.
**Gauge:** 7¼ inch.
**Line Length:** 400 yards, circuit.
**First Opened:** 2005.

| No | Name | Type | Builder | Built |
|----|------|------|---------|-------|
| | | 0-4-0PH | Roanoke | 2004 |

## CARNFUNNOCK FAMILY FUN ZONE MINIATURE RAILWAY

Passengers board at Carnfunnock Halt, which is on one of the loops of this dumb-bell layout.

**Address:** Carnfunnock Country Park, Coast Road, Drains Bay, Ballygally, Larne, County Antrim, BT40 2QG.
**Telephone:** 028 2858 3269.
**OS Grid Ref:** D 384067.
**Operator:** P Johnston.
**Website:** www.carnfunnock.com
**Gauge:** 7¼ inch.
**Line Length:** 500 yards, dumb-bell.
**First Opened:** 1998.

Park entry fee

| No | Name | Type | Builder | Built |
|----|------|------|---------|-------|
| | Colonel Bogey | 6wPH | R Greatrex | 1997 |

▲ Visiting tram 8 is seen at the Drumawhey Junction Railway on 31 July 2011.   **Peter Scott**

# COLERAINE SOCIETY OF MODEL ENGINEERS

This line is a simple circuit from Turnakibbock station. Access to the club house is gained via a foot bridge over the track. A turntable leads to several steaming bays.

**Address:** Turnakibbock, Damhead, Coleraine, County Londonderry.
**Telephone:** 028 7034 4723.
**OS Grid Ref:** C 895303.
**Operator:** Coleraine & District Society of Model Engineers Ltd.
**Gauge:** 3½ inch/5 inch/7¼ inch.
**Line Length:** 600 yards, circular.
**First Opened:** 1990.

# CULTRA LIGHT RAILWAY

The line here runs in and out of a walled garden. The station at Cultra Central has footbridge access to the elevated 3½ inch/5 inch gauge tracks inside the circuit.

**Address:** Ulster Folk and Transport Museum, Cultra, Near Hollywood, County Down, BT18 0EU.
**Telephone:** 028 9042 8428.
**OS Grid Ref:** J 418809.
**Operator:** Model Engineers Society of Northern Ireland.
**Website:** www.nmni.com/uftm
**Gauge:** 7¼ inch.
**Line Length:** 350 yards, circular.
**First Opened:** 1985.

Museum entry fee.

# DELAMONT MINIATURE RAILWAY

A circuit with a tunnel in a country park.

**Address:** Delamont Country Park, Kilyleagh, County Down, BT30 9TZ.
**Telephone:** 028 4482 8333.
**OS Grid Ref:** J 510508.
**Operator:** J Barclay.
**Website:** www.delamontcountrypark.com
**Gauge:** 10¼ inch.
**Line Length:** 1000 yards, circular.
**First Opened:** 1999.

| No | Name | Type | Builder | Built |
|----|------|------|---------|-------|
|    | Freddy | S/O 4wPH | M Stuart | 1984 |

# DRUMAWHEY JUNCTION RAILWAY

The line comprises a circuit off which there is an additional loop. There is one station at Drumawhey Junction, a tunnel, rail over rail bridge, a bridge over a ditch and loading/unloading area. Other features include a turntable, six-road engine/stored shed with an additional four-road carriage shed. The present layout was completed in 2011 and visiting locomotives are welcome by arrangement. The line operates on the first and third Sundays of the month from Easter to the end of September, and also on some Bank Holidays/Public Holidays and all Sundays and Wednesdays in July and August (school holiday time in Northern Ireland). There are also Halloween and Santa trains.

**Address:** Upper Gransha Road, Donaghadee, County Down, BT21 0LZ.
**OS Grid Ref:** J 547761.
**Operator:** Belfast & County Down Miniature Railway Society.
**Website:** www.bcdmrs.org.uk
**Gauge:** 7¼ inch.
**Line Length:** Complex with 3 principal optional circuits of 1470 yards, 2240 yards & 2950 yards.
**First Opened:** 1994.

| No | Name | Type | Builder | Built |
|---|---|---|---|---|
| | Finn MacCool | 0-4-2 | TMA Engineering | 1986 |
| | Reepicheep | 0-4-0ST | S Williamson | 1992 |
| 2 | Edward Phillipson | 2-6-2T+T | Bimpson/Ritchie | 1994 |
| | Lady Grange | 0-6-0T+T | F Stephen | c2000 |
| | Marilyn | 2-4-0T+T | D Tedford | 2003 |
| 1451 | | 0-4-2T | Winson/Ragg | 2008 |
| | Matilda | 0-4-0PH | Roanoke | 1998 |
| | Helios | 0-4-2DH | Roanoke | 1999 |
| | Elektra | 4wPH | Roanoke | 1999 |
| 21 | | 0-4-0+4PMR | H McCauley | 1999 |
| 5 | Merlyn | 0-6-0PH | K Boyd | 2000 |
| | Harlandic | 6wPH | R Greatrex/D Tedford | 2001 |
| | Strathclyde | 6-6wPH | B Lomas | 2003 |
| 102 | Falcon | 4w-4wBE | J Poots/C Smith | 2004 |
| 101 | Eagle | 4w-4wBE | C Smith | 2005 |
| 111 | | 6w-6wBE | J Poots | c2006 |

# JOHN F KENNEDY ARBORETUM MINIATURE RAILWAY

This is an irregular circuit, running from a single station.

**Address:** John F Kennedy Arboretum, New Ross, Near Canpile, County Wexford, Irish Republic.
**Telephone:** (+353) 051 388 171.
**OS Grid Ref:** S 723184.
**Operator:** J F Kennedy Arboretum.
**Website:** www.heritageireland.ie
**Gauge:** 7¼ inch.
**Line Length:** 650 yards, circular.
**First Opened:** 1990.

| No | Name | Type | Builder | Built |
|---|---|---|---|---|
| | Santa Fe | 4-4wPH | B Meyler | 1989 |

▲ 2008 "Pickie Puffer" built by Cromar White stands at the station on the Pickie Family Fun Park Railway on 31 July 2011. **Peter Scott**

# PICKIE FAMILY FUN PARK RAILWAY

The line is a balloon loop with one central station and a halt at the opposite end where there is a turning wye. The park has been undergoing a rebuild, and was due to re-open at Easter 2012.

**Address:** Pickie Family Fun Park, Seafront, Bangor, County Down, BT20 3BJ.
**Telephone:** 028 9127 0069.
**OS Grid Ref:** J 501820.
**Operator:** North Down Borough Council.
**Website:** www.northdowntourism.com
**Gauge:** 7¼ inch.
**Line Length:** 400 yards, balloon loop.
**First Opened:** 1993.

| No | Name | Type | Builder | Built |
|----|------|------|---------|-------|
| 2008 | Pickie Puffer | S/O 2-4-2DH | Cromar White | 2008 |

# TRAMORE MINIATURE RAILWAY

This line runs round a fun park, including a boating lake. There are two tunnel/sheds in which the stock is housed at night. During the season operation often continues into the evenings.

**Address:** Tramore Amusement Park, Seafront, Tramore, County Waterford, Irish Republic.
**Telephone:** (+353) 051 381 572.
**OS Grid Ref:** S 585012.
**Operator:** Tramore Failte Ltd.
**Gauge:** 15 inch.
**Line Length:** 400 yards, circular.
**First Opened:** 1973.

| No | Name | Type | Builder | Built |
|----|------|------|---------|-------|
| | | S/O 2-8-0PH | Severn Lamb | 1973 |

# WESTPORT HOUSE EXPRESS

Trains run from the terminus at Westport Central along a single line and then around a balloon loop next to the lake.

**Address:** Westport House and Childrens Zoo, Westport, Near Knock, County Mayo, Irish Republic.
**Telephone:** (+353) 098 27766.
**OS Grid Ref:** L 987846.
**Operator:** Lord Altamont.
**Website:** www.westporthouse.ie
**Gauge:** 15 inch.
**Line Length:** 700 yards, balloon loop.
**First Opened:** 1990.

Park entry fee

| No | Name | Type | Builder | Built |
|----|------|------|---------|-------|
| | W H | S/O 2-6-0DH | Severn Lamb | 1989 |

# AREA 12: CHANNEL ISLANDS, AND ISLE OF MAN

## ALDERNEY MINIATURE RAILWAY

The railway follows a scenic route in Mannez Quarry, next to the lighthouse. Operation, at weekends when staff are available, coincides with the standard gauge trains of the Alderney Railway from Braye Road. Trains are operated by one petrol locomotive which pulls three sit-astride carriages or a 1st class sit-in carriage.

**Address:** Mannez Quarry, Alderney, Channel Islands.
**Telephone:** 01481 822 978.
**OS Grid Ref:** WA 601087.
**Operator:** Alderney Railway.
**Website:** www.alderneyrailway.com/miniature.htm
**Gauge:** 7¼ inch.
**Line Length:** 400 yards, circular.
**First Opened:** 1995.

| No | Name | Type | Builder | Built |
|----|------|------|---------|-------|
| | Alec Tucker | 0-4-0PH | Roanoke | 1999 |

▲ The Beer Heights Light Railway runs an extensive service during the summer months, especially during the school holidays. On 2 July 2009 2-4-4T No. 9 "Claudine" runs through the attractive gardens with a fully laden train.              **Robert Pritchard**

# SAUSMAREZ MANOR MINIATURE RAILWAY

This line is an oval with one station and two spurs to sheds.

**Address:** Sausmarez Manor, Sausmarez Road, St Martins, Guernsey, Channel Islands, GY4 6SG.
**Telephone:** 01481 235 571.
**OS Grid Ref:** WV 329762.
**Operator:** Sausmarez Manor.
**Website:** www.sausmarezmanor.co.uk
**Gauge:** 7¼ inch.
**Line Length:** 350 yards, circular.
**First Opened:** 1985.

House entry fee.

| No | Name | Type | Builder | Built |
|---|---|---|---|---|
| | NCB | S/O 0-4-0BE | Compass House | 2000 |
| | Remus | 4-4wPH | T Leigh | 1989 |

# THE ORCHID LINE

This line can be found within the Wildlife Park at Ballaugh. Trains follow an ingenious course around loops and over crossovers before returning to the station. The track was further extended over the winter of 1999/2000.

**Address:** Curraghs Wildlife Park, Ballaugh, Isle of Man, IM7 5EA.
**Telephone:** 01624 897 323.
**OS Grid Ref:** SC 367943.
**Operator:** Manx Steam and Model Engineering Club.
**Website:** http://homepages.mcb.net/howe/msmec
**Gauge:** 3½ inch/5 inch/7¼ inch.
**Line Length:** 1100 yards, complex.
**First Opened:** 1992.

Park entry fee.

| No | Name | Type | Builder | Built |
|---|---|---|---|---|
| 8047 | Cushag | 0-4-0ST | D Hill | 1987 |
| | Alice | 0-4-0ST | J Horsfield | 1989 |
| 1366 | Florrie | 0-6-0PT | D Hill | 1989 |
| | Slieaueyder | 0-4-0T | M Casey | 1995 |
| | Thomas/Ardwhallan | 0-4-0ST | C Heard | 2002 |
| 30940 | St.Leonards | 4-4-0 | O'Neill/Spalding | 2002 |
| 93 | Denys | 4wBE | Maxitrak | 1998 |
| 9 | Maurice | 6wPH | R Greatrex | 2001 |
| D1666 | Odin | 4w-4wPE/BE | MS&MEC | 2012 |

# PRIVATE MINIATURE RAILWAYS

The following miniature railway is open to the public on special occasions only. Please do not visit this location except on advertised public opening days.

## STAPLEFORD MINIATURE RAILWAY

One of the most outstanding 10¼ inch gauge railways in the UK, the original line was constructed by the late Lord Gretton, and connected with two model passenger carrying liners on the lake. After the sale of the house the line was remodelled and is now only open to the public on special days. For further details please see the railway's website.

**Address:** Stapleford Park, Stapleford, Near Melton Mowbray, Leicestershire, LE14 2SF.
**OS Grid Ref:** SK 812183.
**Operator:** Friends of the Stapleford Miniature Railway.
**Website:** www.fsmr.org.uk
**Gauge:** 10¼ inch.
**Line Length:** 1¼ miles, balloon loop.
**First Opened:** 1958.

| No | Name | Type | Builder | Built |
|---|---|---|---|---|
| 2943 | Hampton Court | 4-6-0 | G&SLE/Twining | 1939 |
| 751 | John H Gretton | 4-4-2 | D Curwen | 1948 |
| 752 | | 2-8-4 | Coleby Simkins | 1971 |
| 5565 | Victoria | 4-6-0 | Moore/Allcock/Coleby Simkins | 1975 |
| 6019 | | 4-8-4 | J Wilks | 1998 |
| 3103 | Uganda | 2-8-4 | EAR//J Wilks | 2008 |
| | | 2-8-2 | J Wilks | U/C |
| D100 | The White Heron | 4w-4wPM | Curwen & Newbery | 1962 |

# APPENDIX I: MINIATURE RAILWAY SUPPLIERS

The following are miniature railway suppliers that may be of interest if you are starting out in the hobby, or want to build on your current miniature railway or locomotive collection.

Abbots Model Engineering - www.abbotsmodeleng.co.uk

Antique Steam – www.antiquesteam.com

Aristocraft - www.aristocraft.me.uk

Compass House – www.compass-house.co.uk

Cromar White – www.cromarwhite.co.uk

Denver Light Railway – www.denverlightrailway.co.uk

Engineers Emporium – www.engineersemporium.co.uk

Great Northern Steam – www.greatnorthernsteam.co.uk

Knightley Light Railway – www.knightleylightrailway.co.uk

Mardyke – www.mardyke.co.uk

Maxitrak – www.maxitrak.co.uk

Miniature Railway Supply Company – www.miniaturerailwaysupply.com

MJ Engineering – www.mjeng.co.uk

Model Engineering Products (Bexhill) – www.model-engineering.co.uk

MRW Railways - www.mrwrailways.co.uk

Phoneix Locos – www.phoenixlocos.com

PNP Railways – www.pnprailways.co.uk

Ride on Railways – www.rideonrailways.co.uk

Roanoke – www.roanoke.co.uk

Station Road Steam – www.stationroadsteam.co.uk

Steamdays – www.steamdays.co.uk

Steam & Diesel Castings – www.sadcastings.org.uk

Western Steam – www.westernsteam.co.uk

View Models – www.viewmodels.co.uk

# APPENDIX II: SOCIETIES AND PERIODICALS

The following societies and periodicals particularly cater for those interested in miniature railways:

## Narrow Gauge Railway Society

Subscription (2012) £23, includes journals 'Narrow Gauge News' bi-monthly and 'The Narrow Gauge' quarterly.

www.ngrs.org

## 7¼" Gauge Society

Subscription (2012) £25, includes '7¼" Gauge News', quarterly.

www.sevenandaquarter.org

## 10¼ inch Gauge Society

Subscription (2012) £6 a year, includes three newsletter per year.

www.tenandaquarter.org

## The Heywood Society Journal

Bi-annual journal devoted to miniature railway subjects. Annual subscription covers the May and October issues each year, currently (2012) £10.

www.theheywoodsociety.co.uk

## Miniature Railway Magazine

Magazine published three times a year by ATOB Publishing. Subscription (2012) £7.50 per year.

www.miniature-railway.com

## Friends of the Miniature Railway Museum Trust

Membership offers and discounts, plus three issues of Miniature Railway included in £20 (2012) membership.

www.miniaturerailwaymuseum.co.uk/friends

## British Main Line Group

For 1/8 scale British main line locomotives on 7¼ inch gauge track.

www.britishmainlinegroup.org

## Branch Line Society

Annual membership runs from 1st May, various subscription rates. 'Branch Line News', published fortnightly, includes a column on Minor Railways.

www.branchline.org.uk

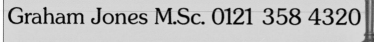